SCHOLASTIC

Spelling™

Louisa Moats and Barbara Foorman

Welcome!

Hardcover ISBN 0-590-34490-0
Softcover ISBN 0-590-34466-8

1 2 3 4 5 6 7 8 9 10   10   03 02 01 00 99 98 97

Contents

Contents

UNIT 3

UNIT 4

Contents

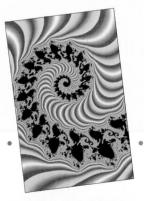

Spelling Strategies
Word Study Path

See the word

See
Look at the letters in the word.

Say
Pronounce the word, and say the letters aloud.
Then say the word in syllables.

Link
Break the word into syllables and meaningful
parts. Mark the prefixes, suffixes, roots, and
endings.

Write
Write the word until it "sticks" in your memory.
Say the letters as you write. Use the word in a
sentence.

Check
Keep a personal spelling journal. Get in the
habit of looking up words you are not sure of.

Write

7

Spelling Words

hour
our
air
heir
aisle
I'll
isle
knead
need
new
knew
gnu   LOOKOUT WORD
ring
wring
plum
plumb
him
hymn
wrapped
rapt

Review	Challenge
delightfully	bite
belief	byte
hoarse	

My Words

_____

_____

_____

Homophones

Ⓐ See and Say

The Spelling Concept

Homophone	Meaning
air	a mix of gases that surrounds Earth
heir	someone who has been left money, land, or a title

Homophones are words that have the same pronunciation but different spellings and meanings. Often homophones sound alike because one word has a silent letter.

The gnu gnawed twigs.

MEMORY JOGGER

Ⓑ Link Sounds and Letters

Say each spelling word. Listen for the words that sound alike. Then sort the words on a chart like the one below. In one column, write the spelling words with silent letters. In the other column, write the homophone that goes with each.

Word Sort

Words With Silent Letters	Homophones

Ⓒ Write and Check

Write your own tongue twister with two or three spelling words that sound identical.

_____

_____

_____

_____

TONGUE TWISTER

I knew that Nellie needed an hour to knead new dough for our nut rolls.

A Build Vocabulary: **Homophones**

Read the sentences below. Replace each underlined word with its correct homophone.

1–2. "Do we have everything we <u>knead</u> for <u>hour</u> climb up the mountain?" I wondered.

3–4. I <u>new</u> the <u>heir</u> at this altitude would be difficult to breathe.

5. I hoped that everyone had <u>rapt</u> his or her belongings carefully.

6–7. I decided to leave my favorite <u>wring</u> at home, but I took a <u>plumb</u> for a snack.

8–9. I noticed the guide up ahead. I saw <u>hymn</u> look at his watch to check the <u>our</u>.

10. <u>Aisle</u> never forget that moment when I looked up and saw what we were about to do.

11. I think I must have looked <u>wrapped</u> and dreamy while I stared at the view before me.

12. Once we got over the mountain, many <u>gnu</u> adventures would be waiting for us.

B Word Study: **Word Meaning**

Read the sentences to find the missing homophones. Refer to your Spelling Dictionary if you need help.

13–14. I'll is the contraction for *I will*, but an _ _ _ _ _ is a passageway between rows of seats, and an _ _ _ _ is a small island.

15. A <u>plum</u> is a kind of fruit, but a _ _ _ _ _ is a lead weight.

16. When you <u>need</u> something, you must have it; but when you _ _ _ _ _ dough, you press, stretch, and fold it.

17. <u>New</u> is something just made; <u>knew</u> is the past tense of *know*; and a _ _ _ is a kind of antelope that lives in Africa.

18. <u>Air</u> is what we breathe, but an _ _ _ _ is someone who has been left money, property, or a title.

19. A <u>ring</u> is a thin band worn around a finger, but when you _ _ _ _ _ something, you squeeze it.

20. <u>Him</u> is a pronoun, but a _ _ _ _ is a song of praise.

Be a Spelling Sleuth

You'd be amazed at all the words that have silent letters! Look for homophones and other words that have silent letters on movie posters, on trading cards, on billboards, and in your own favorite books.

Spell Chat

Join two other classmates, and brainstorm four other homophone pairs, such as **knight** and **night**.

Spelling Words

hour	knew
our	gnu LOOKOUT WORD
air	ring
heir	wring
aisle	plum
I'll	plumb
isle	him
knead	hymn
need	wrapped
new	rapt

Review	Challenge
delightfully	bite
belief	byte
hoarse	

My Words

_____
_____
_____

Spelling Words

hour	knew
our	gnu LOOKOUT WORD
air	ring
heir	wring
aisle	plum
I'll	plumb
isle	him
knead	hymn
need	wrapped
new	rapt

Review	Challenge
delightfully	bite
belief	byte
hoarse	

My Words

_____

_____

_____

Quick Write

Write two sentences about something amusing that you saw, heard, or learned when you were a very small child. Use at least one of the homophone sets.

A Write a Memoir

Try composing your memoir on a computer.

Imagine it is many years from now, and you are writing your memoir. Write about a happy time you remember. Use as many spelling words as you can.

B Proofread

Read the first draft of Amanda's memoir. Find and correct the mistakes she made. Look for four spelling errors, two punctuation errors, and one capitalization error.

Tip
When writing contractions like **I'll**, don't forget the apostrophe to replace the missing letters.

> Once, when I was five, Dad took me to a gnu children's play in town. It was about a lost wring that everyone was trying to find, Before long, the children in the audience were laughing and shouting advice to the players onstage. Even Dad almost fell into the isle because he was laughing so hard. In fact, We both yelled ourselves horse. Ill never forget that experience.

PROOFREADING MARKS

∧	Add
⁁	Add a comma
⌣⌣	Add quotation marks
⊙	Add a period
ℓ	Take out
⌒↗	Move
≡	Capital letter
/	Small letter
¶	Indent

Now proofread your own memoir. Check for spelling, capitalization, and punctuation. Be sure to indent the first line of each paragraph.

A Use the Dictionary: Homophones

Most dictionary entries have respellings to help you pronounce the words. In addition to respellings, the entry for a homophone often provides the other homophones in its group to help you pronounce the word.

aisle /īl/ *noun*

The passage that runs between the rows of seats in a theater, house of worship, aircraft, etc. **Aisle** sounds like **isle** or **I'll**.

In the dictionary entry above, all the homophones for *aisle* are listed at the end. The word without the silent letter helps you to pronounce *aisle*. Which word has no silent letter? _____

In the following homophone group, the word with no silent letter can serve as the pronunciation guide for all the homophones: *knew, gnu, new.* Which word has no silent letter? _____

B Test Yourself

Here is the list of spelling words for this lesson. Write the twenty words in alphabetical order.

hour	knew
our	gnu
air	ring
heir	wring
aisle	plum
I'll	plumb
isle	him
knead	hymn
need	wrapped
new	rapt

For Tomorrow...
Get ready to share the homophones you discovered. Remember to study for your test!

Get Word Wise

Words with silent k, such as knee, knight, and the spelling word knead, come from Old English, spoken in England between A.D. 400 and 1000. At that time, the k was pronounced. Thus, knead might have been pronounced /k-nēd/.

Word Study Strategy

See the word

Say it slowly

Link sounds and letters

Write

Check

END

LESSON 2

Spelling Words

tutor
student
studio
clue
fuel
rude
argue
value
continue
accuse
refuse
suit
fruit
juice
bruise
nuisance
ruin
fluid
tuition
lieutenant LOOKOUT WORD

Review	Challenge
gnu	influence
gloomy	nutrition
through	

My Words

_____

_____

_____

Spellings for /o͞o/ and /yo͞o/

A See and Say

The Spelling Concept

/o͞o/		/yo͞o/
tutor	lieutenant	fuel
clue	ruin	accuse
suit		

The sound /o͞o/ can be spelled *u, ue, ui,* and even *ieu.* Sometimes the spelling *ui* makes the sound /o͞o/ followed by another vowel sound, as in *ruin* (ro͞o in). The sound /yo͞o/ can be spelled *ue* and *u-e.*

B Link Sounds and Letters

Say each spelling word. Find the letters that spell /o͞o/ and /yo͞o/ in each one. Write the words under the correct headings in a chart like this one.

We never argue about the value of friendship

MEMORY JOGGER

Word Sort

/o͞o/				/yo͞o/	
u	ue	ui	ieu	ue	u-e

C Write and Check

Write the spelling words that answer the clues.

What kind of clothing rhymes with *boot*? _ _ _ _

What is an orange? Drop the *s* and add *fr* to find out. _ _ _ _ _

What do you get if you squeeze the orange?
Change the *fr* to *j* and the *t* to *ce*. _ _ _ _ _

Now use these words to write a sentence that rhymes.

_____

_____

A Build Vocabulary: Antonym Analogies

An analogy is a sentence with two pairs of words. The first two words relate to each other in the same way as the second two. The analogies below use antonyms. Complete each analogy with a spelling word.

1. *Obey* is to *disobey* as *allow* is to _____.

2. *Gentle* is to *rough* as *polite* is to _____.

3. *Stop* is to *go* as *interrupt* is to _____.

4. *Release* is to *capture* as *restore* is to _____.

B Word Study: Word Meanings

Read each word meaning below. Then write the spelling word that matches it.

5. say that someone did something wrong

6. flowing liquid

7. what something is worth

8. to disagree with someone

9. set of matching clothes

10. a teacher who gives private lessons

11. one who studies

12. a military officer

13. payment for instruction

14. liquid from a fruit

15. something that helps provide an answer

16. something used for heat or energy

17. where an artist works

18. fleshy, juicy product of a plant

19. dark mark on skin

20. annoying person or thing

Be a Spelling Sleuth

Look in sports and health magazines for words that include /o͞o/ and /yo͞o/. Make a list of the words you find.

Spell Chat

Challenge a partner to make up a funny sentence in which words with the /o͞o/ or /yo͞o/ sound are spelled the same way. An example is "A cute mule doesn't have to follow rules." Then you try, using a different spelling pattern from the one your partner chose.

Spelling Words

tutor	refuse
student	suit
studio	fruit
clue	juice
fuel	bruise
rude	nuisance
argue	ruin
value	fluid
continue	tuition
accuse	lieutenant

Review	Challenge
gnu	influence
gloomy	nutrition
through	

My Words

_____

_____

_____

Spelling Words

tutor	refuse
student	suit
studio	fruit
clue	juice
fuel	bruise
rude	nuisance
argue	ruin
value	fluid
continue	tuition
accuse	lieutenant

Review	Challenge
gnu	influence
gloomy	nutrition
through	

My Words

_____

_____

_____

Quick Write

Jot down some adjectives that you could use in a description of someone or something. Then write at least one sentence of description using those adjectives, such as *cute* and *blue*.

A Write a Description of Two Characters

You may wish to write your description on a computer.

Write a brief description of yourself and someone else. Are you as alike as two peas in a pod? Or are you as different as night and day? Choose characteristics that show how you're *similar to* or *different from* each other. Use apostrophes in possessive nouns.

B Proofread

Read the first paragraph of Ben's description. He made four spelling errors and one punctuation error, and he repeated one word that must be taken out.

Tip

To form a singular possessive noun, add 's (father's). To make a regular plural noun possessive, add ' (friends').

My brother Ty and I are both different and alike. Ty is a great math studint, but I need a tuter to pass math. He loves music, but I prefer art. We are both calm and and hate to argeu. Sometimes he can be so gloome, while most of the time I am happy. My dads opinion is that we are different enough not to be mistaken for each other, but alike enough to be brothers.

PROOFREADING MARKS

∧ Add
⅄ Add a comma
⌄⌄ Add quotation marks
⊙ Add a period
ℓ Take out
↻ Move
≡ Capital letter
/ Small letter
¢ Indent

Now proofread your description. Check for spelling, capitalization, and punctuation. Check the apostrophes on those possessive nouns!

A Use the Dictionary:
Alphabetizing

Alphabetizing is a great way to organize words. Some word lists can be alphabetized just by noting the first letter of each word. To alphabetize other word lists, though, you need to go to the second, third, fourth, or more letters.

Which word would come first on a dictionary page, *argue* or *armor*? _____

How do you know? _____

B Test Yourself

Read the incomplete spelling words below. Supply the missing letters that create /o͞o/ or /yo͞o/. Write each complete word.

1. contin _ _

2. t _ _ tion

3. st _ dent

4. fr _ _ t

5. acc _ s _

6. l _ _ _ tenant

7. r _ _ n

8. s _ _ t

9. arg _ _

10. n _ _ sance

11. val _ _

12. r _ d _

13. cl _ _

14. f _ el

15. fl _ _ d

16. st _ dio

17. j _ _ ce

18. ref _ s _

19. t _ tor

20. br _ _ se

Get Word Wise

Lieutenant comes to the English language by way of French. In French, the word **tenir** means "to hold," and **lieu** means "place." In the military, a lieutenant "holds the place of" his or her superior officer, a captain.

Word Study Strategy

See the word

Say it slowly

Link sounds and letters

Write

Check

END

For Tomorrow...
Share some of the words you collected, and invite a partner to guess where you found them. Remember to study for your test!

More Homophones

Spelling Words

rain
rein
reign
vain
vane
vein
claws
clause
morning
mourning
heard
herd
roll
role
straight
strait
great
grate
crews
cruise LOOKOUT WORD

Review	Challenge
lieutenant	sleight
unusual	slight
weight	

My Words

_____

_____

_____

A See and Say

The Spelling Concept

Homophone	Spellings of /ā/	Meaning
rain	ai	water that falls from clouds
rein	ei	one of two straps attached to a bridle
reign	eig	to rule as a king or queen

Homophones are words that are pronounced the same but have different spellings and meanings. Sometimes different spelling patterns can make the same sound in each group of homophones.

A cat has claws at the ends of its paws, but a comma makes the pause at the end of a clause.

MEMORY JOGGER

B Link Sounds and Letters

Say each spelling word. Listen to the sound the vowels make in each word. Then sort the words according to vowel sound on a chart like this one. Check the Spelling Dictionary for pronunciation respellings.

Word Sort

/ā/	/ô/	/û/	/ō/	/o͞o/

C Write and Check

Read this riddle and its answer. Then use homophones to write a riddle of your own.

_____

_____

_____

RIDDLE

Why is a fireplace store such a great place to shop?

because it has grate prices

Vocabulary Practice

A Build Vocabulary: Word Meanings

Complete each sentence with the missing homophones. Check your Spelling Dictionary if you need help.

The sailors took their ship ___1___ through the narrow ___2___.

The ___3___ on each ship decided to take a holiday ___4___.

The rancher ___5___ his ___6___ of cattle running.

A ___7___ in our contract with Elroy the Cat says he must never use his ___8___ while on stage.

Carlos was so ___9___ that if the weather ___10___ showed a strong wind, he would go inside rather than mess up his hair.

Be a Spelling Sleuth

Look for homophones on product labels and recipes. Try also to find homophones in the books and articles you are reading at home.

B Word Study: Word Endings

Adding a word ending to a base word can change the word's meaning and part of speech. Look at the word endings below. Then read the sentences. Add the proper ending to each underlined word so the sentence makes sense. Then write the word.

-er means "more than"   *-s* means plural

-ed means "in the past"   *-ing* means "act of doing"

Spell Chat
Challenge a partner to say a sentence that has a homophone in it, such as "I enjoy walking in the rain." Ask him or her to spell the homophone.

11. We stayed indoors because it was <u>rain</u>.

12. Patty and Tim had <u>roll</u> down the hill.

13. A <u>great</u> number of people will shop today than yesterday.

14. Pablo played many <u>role</u> in the play.

15. The Solas family replaced two fireplace <u>grate</u> in their home.

16. The king has been <u>reign</u> for many years.

17. Pietro pulled back the <u>rein</u> on his horse.

18. He found some rich <u>vein</u> of gold in the mountain.

C Write

Write a sentence that rhymes using the words *mourning* and *morning*.

_____

_____

Spelling Words	
rain	heard
rein	herd
reign	roll
vain	role
vane	straight
vein	strait
claws	great
clause	grate
morning	crews
mourning	cruise

Review	Challenge
lieutenant	sleight
unusual	slight
weight	

My Words

_____

_____

_____

Spelling Words

rain	heard
rein	herd
reign	roll
vain	role
vane	straight
vein	strait
claws	great
clause	grate
morning	crews
mourning	cruise

LOOKOUT WORD

Review	Challenge
lieutenant	sleight
unusual	slight
weight	

My Words

_____

_____

_____

Quick Write

Write two sentences describing the next amazing feat that your tall-tale character performs. Include a homophone group from the spelling list.

A Describe a Tall-Tale Character

Try composing your opening on a computer.

Create your own character who's "bigger than life." Write the opening of a tall tale. Concentrate on the character's appearance and personality. Brainstorm some spelling words you might use in your opening, and remember to watch out for run-on sentences!

B Proofread

Read the first part of Kenesha's tale, and correct her errors. Find four spelling errors, one error in capitalization, and one run-on sentence.

Tip

A run-on sentence is two or more complete thoughts run together without correct punctuation. To fix a run-on, make two complete sentences.

> Once there was a stonecutter who had an unusaul daughter. One mourning, when she was only five, she went strait into her father's Workshop and got right to work. With one swing of the hammer, she cut a huge rock into ten neat blocks when the villagers herd what the girl was doing, they all gathered near the stonecutter's shop to watch her work.

PROOFREADING MARKS

∧	Add
⌁	Add a comma
⌄⌄	Add quotation marks
⊙	Add a period
ℓ	Take out
⟳	Move
≡	Capital letter
/	Small letter
¢	Indent

Now proofread the description of your own tall-tale character. Check spelling, capitalization, and punctuation. Watch for run-on sentences!

A Use the Dictionary: More Alphabetizing

You've already alphabetized words by the first, second, and third letter. Sometimes, however, two words share the same first three letters. Then you must look at the fourth letter of each word to decide which word comes first.

Which word would come first on a dictionary page, *claws* or *clause*? _____.

How do you know? _____

Write each pair of homophones below in alphabetical order.

vane _____   roll _____

vain _____   role _____

reign _____   heard _____

rein _____   herd _____

B Test Yourself

Read the short definitions below. Write the spelling word that matches each definition.

1. fireplace bottom
2. feeling sorrow or grief
3. work teams on ships
4. group of animals
5. carries blood through body
6. to rule as king or queen
7. pointer showing wind direction
8. water falling from clouds
9. nails on animal's foot
10. to move by turning over
11. one part of a sentence
12. not bent or curved
13. very good or wonderful
14. part a person plays
15. a trip on a ship
16. narrow strip of water
17. past tense of *hear*
18. time of day between midnight and noon
19. straps on a bridle
20. proud of the way you look

For Tomorrow...
Share some words you found, and challenge a partner to spell them. Remember to study for your test!

Get Word Wise

Rain is a word we inherited from the Anglo-Saxons, a Germanic tribe that settled in England during the Middle Ages. The Anglo-Saxons spoke Old English. *Rain* was spelled *ren*, because *e* had the sound /ā/. Later, influenced by French, the *e* was replaced by /ai/.

Word Study Strategy

See the word

Say it slowly

Link sounds and letters

Write

Check

END

Spelling Words

liar
polar
molar
solar
lunar
scholar
beggar
burglar
calendar
regular
popular
similar
familiar
particular
peculiar
singular
muscular
circular
rectangular
nuclear *LOOKOUT WORD*

Review	Challenge
cruise	similarity
colorful	familiarity
caterpillar	

My Words

_____

_____

_____

Words That End With ar

A See and Say

The Spelling Concept

Word	Pronunciation
molar	/mō lər/
familiar	/fə mil yər/

When the final syllable of a word is unaccented and includes the letters ar, ar is usually pronounced /ər/. If the final syllable includes the letters iar, ar is usually pronounced /yər/.

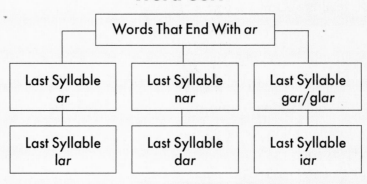

To mark a particular date, put a star on your calendar.

MEMORY JOGGER

B Link Sounds and Letters

Say each spelling word, and listen for the final syllable. Sometimes it includes a letter before *ar*. Sort the words on a chart like the one below.

Word Sort

Words That End With ar

Last Syllable ar	Last Syllable nar	Last Syllable gar/glar

Last Syllable lar	Last Syllable dar	Last Syllable iar

C Write and Check

Write the spelling words in the tongue twister.

_____

Use some spelling words to write a tongue twister of your own.

_____

_____

TONGUE TWISTER

Patty was in particular partial to that peculiar yet popular polar bear at the zoo.

Ⓐ Build Vocabulary: **Synonyms**

Synonyms are words that have the same or almost the same meaning. Read each word or words below. Then write the spelling word that is its synonym. Use the Spelling Dictionary if you need help.

1. icy region
2. schedule
3. fibber
4. moonlike
5. athletic

6. atomic energy
7. thief
8. tooth
9. sunny
10. panhandler

Be a Spelling Sleuth

Look for words that end in **ar** in a weather report or in sports or science magazines and in computer software programs on outer space and the climate.

Ⓑ Word Study: **Forming Adverbs**

An adverb is a word that can describe a verb or an adjective. Adverbs often end in -*ly*. Write the spelling word from which the adverb came.

11. The author Samuel Clemens was <u>popularly</u> known as Mark Twain.

12. <u>Similarly</u>, sports stars are often known by nicknames.

13. Maria was <u>peculiarly</u> sensitive about the old hat she wore.

14. Don was not <u>particularly</u> excited about going to the soccer game.

15. Around the neighborhood, Talia was <u>familiarly</u> known as "Speedy" after she won two track meets.

16. The marimba players moved <u>circularly</u> around the table.

17. The architect designed a <u>rectangularly</u> shaped office building.

18. Jenny took a <u>scholarly</u> approach to her studies.

19. JoJo was <u>singularly</u> responsible for the band's success.

20. The Native American Cultural Heritage Club met <u>regularly</u> twice a month.

Spell Chat
Challenge the person next to you to name other words that end in **ar**.

Spelling Words

liar	popular
polar	similar
molar	familiar
solar	particular
lunar	peculiar
scholar	singular
beggar	muscular
burglar	circular
calendar	rectangular
regular	nuclear *LOOKOUT WORD*

Review	Challenge
cruise	similarity
colorful	familiarity
caterpillar	

My Words

_____
_____
_____

Spelling Words

liar	popular
polar	similar
molar	familiar
solar	particular
lunar	peculiar
scholar	singular
beggar	muscular
burglar	circular
calendar	rectangular
regular	nuclear *LOOKOUT WORD*

Review	Challenge
cruise	similarity
colorful	familiarity
caterpillar	

My Words

_____

_____

_____

Quick Write

Write two sentences about someone in your school whom you admire. Use a word that ends with *ar* in each sentence, and try to include a series of three items that need to be separated by commas.

A Write a Biographical Sketch

Use a computer to design graphics for your sketch.

You know someone with many fine qualities that he or she puts to use through actions. Write a biographical sketch of this person. Describe what the person does that shows his or her fine qualities. Remember to use commas to separate items in a series when you write.

B Proofread

Proofread the first part of Janell's biographical sketch. She made four spelling errors, two punctuation errors, and one capitalization error.

> **Tip**
> Remember, commas are used to separate items in a series, to set off nouns of direct address, and to set off introductory words.

Mrs. Johnson is a reguler hero in our neighborhood. She's helped dogs birds cats and even a caterpilar. She's a familer face at the local senior center. She always has a smile for everyone and offers help whenever it is needed. Mrs. johnson isn't rich. but she gives others everything she can. She is a very populer person in the community.

PROOFREADING MARKS

∧	Add
⌄	Add a comma
⌄⌄	Add quotation marks
⊙	Add a period
ℓ	Take out
◯⌒	Move
≡	Capital letter
/	Small letter
¢	Indent

Now proofread your own biographical sketch. Check your spelling, capitalization, and punctuation.

A Use the Dictionary: **Guide Words**

The words at the top of a dictionary page are called guide words. They show you the first and last entry on that page. The other entries on the page come between the two guide words in alphabetical order.

Read the guide words on this dictionary page. Which words below the guide words would also be found on this page?

silversmith ▶ sinister

solar   scholar   similar   singular

B Test Yourself

Write the spelling words that would be found between each pair of words below. Alphabetize the words.

1–3. false/luster

_____
_____
_____

4–9. palm/right

_____
_____
_____
_____
_____
_____

10–13. apple/circus

_____
_____
_____
_____

14–16. mercy/number

_____
_____
_____

17–20. scare/talent

_____
_____
_____

For Tomorrow...
Get ready to share the words ending with **ar** that you found. Remember to study for your test!

Get Word Wise

The words nuclear and nucleus both come from nux, the Latin word for "nut" or "kernel." Just as the nut of a tree is located in the center of its seed, the nucleus is located in the center of an atom.

Word Study Strategy

See the word

Say it slowly

Link sounds and letters

Write

Check

END

LESSON 5

Spelling Words

strong
strength
long
length
wide
width
deep
depth
true
truth
laugh
laughter
speak
speech
behave
behavior
prove — LOOKOUT WORD
proof
proud
pride

Review	Challenge
nuclear	steal
truly	stealth
pleasant	

My Words

_____
_____
_____

Related Words

A See and Say

The Spelling Concept

Word	Meaning	Related Word	Meaning
wide	large from side to side	width	distance from one side to the other
long	large from top to bottom	length	distance from top to bottom

Many adjectives and verbs have related nouns. Often the related words contain different vowel sounds.

B Link Sounds and Letters

Say each pair of related words. Listen for the similarities and differences in pronunciation. Then sort your spelling words on a chart.

We need to laugh. No one ever gets enough laughter!

MEMORY JOGGER

Word Sort

Related Words With Same Vowel Sound	Related Words With Different Vowel Sounds

C Write and Check

Write a conversation that Carol and Ms. Swanson could have about the pool. Use three spelling words in each speech bubble.

Ⓐ Build Vocabulary: **Parts of Speech**

The meanings below will give you practice in using the related words on your spelling list. Write the word that fits each meaning.

1. to make a sound showing that something is funny (verb)

2. the sound you hear after someone tells a joke (noun)

3. the way you feel when you've done something well (adjective)

4. a feeling of self-respect and achievement (noun)

5. to act properly (verb)

6. the way you act (noun)

7. from one end to the other (adjective)

8. distance from one end of something to the other (noun)

9. the real facts (noun)

10. agreeing with the facts (adjective)

Ⓑ Word Study:
Word Endings and Suffixes

Add the ending or suffix to each word below. Then write the whole word.

11. Add -est to *strong.*

12. Add -en to *strength.*

13. Add -er to *wide.*

14. Add -s to *width.*

15. Add -en to *deep.*

16. Add -s to *depth.*

17. Add -ing to *speak.*

18. Add -less to *speech.*

19. Add -s to *prove.*

20. Add -s to *proof.*

Spell Chat

With a partner, brainstorm other pairs of related words. Try adding endings to them to make new words.

Be a Spelling Sleuth

Keep an eye out this week for words that are related. Look for them on video, CD, or audiotape packages, and on labels of all kinds. Keep a list of the pairs you find.

Spelling Words	
strong	laugh
strength	laughter
long	speak
length	speech
wide	behave
width	behavior
deep	prove
depth	proof
true	proud
truth	pride

Review	Challenge
nuclear	steal
truly	stealth
pleasant	

My Words

_____

_____

_____

Spelling Words

strong	laugh
strength	laughter
long	speak
length	speech
wide	behave
width	behavior
deep	prove
depth	proof
true	proud
truth	pride

prove — LOOKOUT WORD

Review	Challenge
nuclear	steal
truly	stealth
pleasant	

My Words

_____

_____

_____

Quick Write

Write two sentences about a visit to the future. Include at least one pair of related spelling words. For example, *We took a* **wide** *spaceship to Mars. The* **width** *of the ship allowed us to get up and play catch.*

A Write a Postcard

 Try composing your message on a computer.

Imagine this! You're an explorer from either the past or the future. Write a postcard home in which you tell about a discovery you made. Try to include the four sentence types.

B Proofread

Read William's postcard from the future. He made four spelling mistakes, one error in capitalization, and one error in punctuation. Correct them.

Tip

A declarative sentence makes a statement, an interrogative one asks a question, an imperative one expresses a command, and an exclamatory sentence expresses strong feelings.

> It is the year 2595. I have just returned from a pleasent visit to the planet Earth. I am amazed to find that the people there are known for speaking the trooth. It's ture. They will never hurt anyone's feelings. Best of all, they are full of joy and lafter. What a wonderful discovery! Aren't you glad to know that Someday Earthlings will really live in peace.

PROOFREADING MARKS

∧	Add
⸝	Add a comma
⸌⸍	Add quotation marks
⊙	Add a period
ℓ	Take out
⟲	Move
≡	Capital letter
/	Small letter
⸿	Indent

Now proofread your own postcard. Check spelling, capitalization, and punctuation.

Ⓐ Use the Dictionary: **Entry Words**

The words defined in a dictionary are called entry words. Entry words are always arranged in alphabetical order. Each entry contains a pronunciation of the word, names its part of speech, provides a definition, and sometimes gives a sample sentence.

proof /proof/ *noun*
Facts or evidence that something is true. *The lawyer claimed to have proof that his client was innocent. Do you have proof of your age?*

prove /proov/ *verb*
To show that something is true. *The experiment proved our hypothesis. The lawyer tried to prove that her client was innocent.* ▷ **proving, proved**

Choose one of the word pairs below. Look up the words' entries in your Spelling Dictionary. Then write a sentence for each word you looked up.

strong/strength   true/truth   speak/speech   proud/pride

_____

_____

Ⓑ Test Yourself

Read each word. Then write the related word from the spelling list.

1. laughter
2. behave
3. prove
4. depth
5. laugh
6. deep
7. wide
8. proof
9. behavior
10. long
11. speak
12. truth

13. pride
14. width
15. strength
16. true

17. strong
18. speech
19. length
20. proud

For Tomorrow...
Get ready to share the related words you found on labels of all kinds. Remember to study for your test!

Get Word Wise

In Latin, the word *stringere* means "to bind tight." When the Anglo-Saxons adopted this word into Old English, they spelled it *strong* or *strang*, and used it to mean physical and mental strength, just as we do today.

Word Study Strategy

See the word

Say it slowly

Link sounds and letters

Write

Check

END

The Peculiar Rich Man's Heir

Complete each paragraph with spelling words.

heir	isle	knew
peculiar	strong	behavior

Bennington Wick had been the richest man in the world, but also one of the most **(1)** . For the past 40 years, he had lived off the coast of Florida on his own private **(2)** . When it was discovered that he had died, at the ripe old age of 95, no one **(3)** who the **(4)** to his fortune was. He had never had children, and his odd **(5)** kept him from forming **(6)** ties to anyone.

wrapped	heard	speak	prove	proof

As soon as some of his distant relatives **(7)** that Wick had died, they appeared at the office of his lawyer. Each one came to **(8)** that he or she should inherit Wick's fortune. The lawyer said he would **(9)** with each one. If the **(10)** that a person offered seemed strong, the lawyer would explain about the videotape he had found **(11)** in a note that read, "To be viewed after my death." Not even the lawyer had seen the tape.

air	rapt	argue	continue
herd	straight	strength	laughter

Tension filled the **(12)** as all the fortune seekers gathered to view the tape. They sat in **(13)** attention, staring at the screen. The tape began with shots of a **(14)** of unusual sheep with **(15)** horns. Someone burst into nervous **(16)** when Wick himself began speaking. Wick explained that these sheep were rare and endangered. Then he said that his entire fortune would go to making sure that the sheep would **(17)** to exist. People in the audience started to **(18)** that they should have the money, but their arguments lost their **(19)** against the videotape that made Wick's wishes clear.

Homophone Pairs

clause	knead
reign	isle
aisle	claws
need	rein

Homophones are words that sound alike but have different spellings and meanings. Write homophone pairs to complete the sentences below.

1. A cat has _____, but a sentence has a _____.

2. You can walk around an ocean _____ or walk down a movie theater's _____.

3. A king can _____ in his kingdom. A rider can _____ in his horse.

4. To make dough, you _____ to use flour. To make bread, you have to _____ the dough.

The Art Theft

The writer of this story wasn't sure how to spell some words. Every underlined word is a possible spelling. Write the correctly spelled word on the lines below the story.

Police have caught up with the man they suspect of being the **(5)** burglar, berglar who broke into an artist's **(6)** studeo, studio last week. He was arrested as he tried to board a **(7)** crews, cruise ship sailing through a **(8)** strait, straight. A young **(9)** studint, student working as a waiter in a **(10)** popular, populer local restaurant provided the tip that led to the arrest. He called the police when a **(11)** musclar, muscular man with a **(12)** rectangular, rectanguler suitcase came into the restaurant. The man looked **(13)** familure, familiar to the boy. "He was very **(14)** vain, vane," the waiter said. "He kept telling the waitress how clever he was. Then I remembered seeing his picture in the paper some months ago. He had been a robbery suspect." The police detective said the suspect may also be accused of a break-in at a **(15)** solur, solar power plant where an experimental weather **(16)** vain, vane was stolen.

WORD MATH

Find the answer to this riddle by doing "word math."

She can read Latin and recite a poem from memory while standing on her head. Who is she?

supper - p   s+choke-ke+lar =

_____   _____

5. _____   9. _____   13. _____

6. _____   10. _____   14. _____

7. _____   11. _____   15. _____

8. _____   12. _____   16. _____

Read All About It!

News stories need clever or strong headlines to attract readers' attention. Write a headline for each news story summarized below. Use at least one spelling word on the newspaper for each headline.

DAILY ☀ SUN
★★★

gnu	scholar
speech	behave
nuisance	molar
ruin	juice
lieutenant	crews
calendar	argue
laugh	proud

1. An earthquake damages part of the ancient city of Rome, Italy.

_____

2. A new animal at the conservation park causes a disturbance.

_____

3. An excellent student addresses the sixth-grade graduating class.

_____

4. A military officer tells a very funny joke at a news conference.

_____

5. A famous politician has dental surgery.

_____

6. An important sailboat race ends in an argument.

_____

7. The president declares a new holiday.

_____

Tip
Remember to capitalize all important words in a headline.

Look back at the words you misspelled in your Unit 1 Posttests and at your My Words, Review Words, and Challenge Words. Use them to write more headlines.

_____

_____

_____

Nose for News

Write a short news story for one of your headlines. Proofread it for spelling, capitalization, grammar, and punctuation. Work with others to create a newspaper featuring all your stories.

PROOFREADING MARKS

∧	Add
⩞	Add a comma
ⱽⱽ	Add quotation marks
⊙	Add a period
ℓ	Take out
↻	Move
≡	Capital letter
/	Small letter
⊄	Indent

Homophones

Read what Jessica says. Write the right word to complete each sentence.

wrapped   rapt

1. The box was _____ in gold paper.

2. Everyone watched with _____ attention as he opened his present.

rein   reign

3. The people longed for the end of the evil queen's _____.

4. No one could _____ in her power!

straight   strait

5. The ship was to sail _____ to Hong Kong.

6. To do so, it had to sail through the _____.

aisle   isle

7. Don't trip in the _____ when you accept the award!

8. Your story about living on an _____ deserved to win.

claws   clause

9. A bear needs its _____ if it's going to catch its prey.

10. *If it's going to catch its prey* is a _____ in a sentence.

crews   cruise

11. Two ships _____ from Seattle to Alaska.

12. Both ships have excellent _____ on board.

Jessica says...

I wrote to my best friend Emma saying that I <u>herd</u> that Michelle, Tammy, and Lucia were coming to her party. She wrote back to say that she didn't know that these girls were sheep.

I guess that was Emma's way of telling me I should have spelled <u>herd</u> <u>h-e-a-r-d</u>!

Spelling Matters!

Spelling Words

bicycle
icicle
example
idle
idol ✦ LOOKOUT WORD
single
principle
principal
animal
normal
hospital
numeral
several
level
barrel
model
shovel
novel
travel
vowel

Review	Challenge
prove	colonial
peacefully	colonel
whistle	

My Words

_____
_____
_____

Learn and Spell

Words With /əl/

Ⓐ See and Say

The Spelling Concept

le bicycle	ol idol
al numeral	el shovel

The sound of schwa, *uh*, is the weak vowel sound you hear in most unstressed syllables. It is often followed by /l/ at the end of a word; /əl/ can be spelled *le*, *ol*, *al*, or *el*.

> Don't put a normal animal in the hospital.

MEMORY JOGGER

Ⓑ Link Sounds and Letters

Say each spelling word. Listen for /əl/. Then write the words in the correct column on a chart like this one.

Word Sort

-le Words	-ol Words	-al Words	-el Words

Ⓒ Write and Check

Which spelling word makes sense in each statement? Use the underlined letters as clues to the missing word.

The _ _ _ _ _ _ _ _ _ at school is my p<u>al</u>.

A ru<u>le</u> of law is a legal _ _ _ _ _ _ _ _ _.

Now you have <u>l</u>earned by _ _ _ _ _ _ _.

Make up a word puzzle like the ones above with spelling words and "clue" words.

_____
_____
_____

A Build Vocabulary: Word Meanings

Write the spelling word that best fits each clue.

1. a frozen object that hangs from a tree or building
2. a nurse works here
3. the letter *a, e, i, o,* or *u*
4. use it to pick up dirt
5. the head of a school
6. a written number
7. more than one or two
8. a model to be followed
9. usual or regular
10. someone who is adored
11. a creature
12. a rule of law

B Word Study: Words Ending in -ing

The words below were formed by adding *-ing* to some of your spelling words. Write the spelling words from which they came. Notice what happened to words that ended in *le* when *-ing* was added—the *e* was dropped.

13. bicycling
14. idling
15. leveling
16. modeling
17. shoveling
18. traveling

C Write

Write two questions using *single* and *barrel*. Add at least two other /əl/ words to your questions.

_____

_____

_____

> **Spell Chat**
> Think of two phrases that contain spelling words. Challenge a partner to spell the /əl/ words.

Be a Spelling Sleuth

Words that end with /əl/, such as shovel, are all around you. The next time you're in a hardware store or a supermarket, set a time limit—say, three minutes—and see how many /əl/ words you can spot in displays or on the shelves. Write them down.

Spelling Words

bicycle	hospital
icicle	numeral
example	several
idle	level
idol	barrel
single	model
principle	shovel
principal	novel
animal	travel
normal	vowel

Review	Challenge
prove	colonial
peacefully	colonel
whistle	

My Words

_____

_____

_____

Spelling Words

bicycle	hospital
icicle	numeral
example	several
idle	level
idol	barrel
single	model
principle	shovel
principal	novel
animal	travel
normal	vowel

Review	Challenge
prove	colonial
peacefully	colonel
whistle	

My Words

_____

_____

_____

Quick Write

Write three action-packed sentences about your detective's amazing crime-solving abilities. Use as many spelling words as you can.

Ⓐ Write a Character Description

Try composing your description on a computer.

You're a best-selling mystery writer who is creating a new series. Who will be the detective in your stories? Describe that person. Use some spelling words in your description. Make sure your sentences end in the correct punctuation.

Ⓑ Proofread

Read the opening of Marianna's description of a detective she created for a new mystery series. She made four spelling errors, one punctuation error, and one capitalization error. Correct them.

> **Tip**
> Remember that a declarative sentence makes a statement and should end in a period.

Detective Jane gonzales is a former fashion modle. She is the daughter of a high school principle and an animle trainer. Because of this unusual background, she brings to her job a combination of charm, intelligence, and courage She wins hearts, but it is through her skills that she will proof her worth.

PROOFREADING MARKS

∧	Add
⋏	Add a comma
⌄⌄	Add quotation marks
⊙	Add a period
ℓ	Take out
◠↗	Move
≡	Capital letter
/	Small letter
¶	Indent

Now proofread your description of a detective. Check your spelling, punctuation, and capitalization.

Ⓐ Use the Dictionary: **Example Sentence**

Here's a dictionary entry for the word *principal*. It has two meanings. The example sentence shows you how to use the word correctly. It also helps you distinguish *principal* from its homophone, *principle*, which means "a basic truth, law, or belief."

> **prin·ci·pal** /prin sə pəl/
>
> **1. adjective** Most important, chief, or main. *She is a principal dancer with the ballet company.* **adverb** principally. **2. noun** The head of a public school. **Principal** sounds like **principle**.

Write an example sentence for each definition of the word *principal*. Make sure each sentence helps to clarify the meaning of the word.

_____

_____

Ⓑ Test Yourself

Fill in the missing letters to make a spelling word. Then write the complete word.

1. numer – –
2. trav – –
3. examp – –
4. id – – (not busy)
5. id – – (someone who is adored)
6. barr – –
7. princip – – (basic truth or rule)
8. princip – – (most important, or head of school)
9. mod – –
10. norm – –
11. hospit – –
12. bicyc – –
13. sever – –
14. vow – –
15. sing – –
16. anim – –
17. shov – –
18. nov – –
19. icic – –
20. lev – –

For Tomorrow...
Get ready to share the /əl/ words you found in the hardware store or supermarket. Remember to study for the test!

Word Study Strategy

See the word

Say it slowly

Link sounds and letters

Write

Check

END

LESSON 8

Spelling Words

actor
author
director
doctor
donor
explorer
gardener
hiker
janitor
conductor
operator
painter
plumber
professor
radiator
refrigerator
runner
sculptor   LOOKOUT WORD
sailor
tailor

Review	Challenge
idol	predator
heir	competitor
elevator	

My Words

_____

_____

Words With /ər/

A   See and Say

The Spelling Concept

-er	hiker	painter
-or	actor	radiator

When /ər/ is heard at the end of a word, that sound may be spelled or or er. The suffixes -er and -or mean "one who does" or "something that does."

The actor wore orange, and the doctor wore white.

MEMORY JOGGER

B   Link Sounds and Letters

Say each spelling word, and listen for /ər/. Look at each word to see how /ər/ is spelled. Then write the spelling words in the correct column in a chart like this one.

Word Sort

-or Words	-er Words

C   Write and Check

Now make up your own riddle or joke, using one or more of the spelling words.

_____

_____

_____

_____

_____

_____

RIDDLE

Why did the doctor phone the plumber?

He wanted to talk to a drain surgeon.

A Build Background:
Making Relationships

Write the spelling word that relates to each group of words.

1. sink, pipe, faucet
2. waiting room, surgery, medicine
3. cleaning, maintenance, school
4. sew, hem, thread
5. novel, article, best-seller
6. chisel, stone, clay
7. college, teacher, campus
8. plants, seeds, hoe
9. brush, canvas, colors

B Word Study:
Base Words

You can add a suffix to a base word to form a new word. For example, when you add -er to the base word *own*, you form *owner*. Write the spelling word that is formed by adding -er or -or to each underlined word below.

10. radiate heat
11. explore a new continent
12. hike up a trail
13. run a marathon
14. direct a play
15. conduct an orchestra
16. refrigerate food
17. sail a boat
18. act in a play
19. donate to charity
20. operate a machine

Be a Spelling Sleuth

Look in magazines and newspaper classified ads for words ending in /ər/ that have to do with an occupation. For example: *park ranger, editor, decorator* or *teacher.*

Spell Chat

Challenge the person next to you to name three other occupations that end in -er or -or and to tell you their base words.

Spelling Words

actor	operator
author	painter
director	plumber
doctor	professor
donor	radiator
explorer	refrigerator
gardener	runner
hiker	sculptor
janitor	sailor
conductor	tailor

Review	Challenge
idol	predator
heir	competitor
elevator	

My Words

_____

_____

_____

Spelling Words

actor	operator
author	painter
director	plumber
doctor	professor
donor	radiator
explorer	refrigerator
gardener	runner
hiker	sculptor
janitor	sailor
conductor	tailor

Review	Challenge
idol	predator
heir	competitor
elevator	

My Words

_____
_____
_____

Quick Write

Write a three-sentence summary of a movie you have seen. Use as many spelling words as possible. For example, *An explorer and a hiker, lost on a mountain top, find a hidden city.*

A Write a Description of a Movie Scene

You may wish to do this activity on a computer.

You're a screenwriter. Describe what happens in a scene from your latest movie. Tell when and where the scene takes place. Use some spelling words to give information about your characters. Remember, when a sentence has more than two subjects, add commas between them.

B Proofread

Read Anthony's description of a scene in a movie. He made four spelling errors, two punctuation errors, and one capitalization error. Correct them.

Tip
When you write a compound subject, such as Jack, Sarah, and I, be sure to put commas between its parts.

> Hattie McCoy, her dog and her cat live near the Texas coast. Hattie works as a plumer but dreams of becoming an exploror and going to sea. in one scene she discovers that she is the hair to a fortune. Hattie quits her job She buys a boat and names it The Blue Dream. Then Hattie and her pets set sail to Mexico. She's a sailer at last.

PROOFREADING MARKS

∧	Add
⍋	Add a comma
⬙⬙	Add quotation marks
⊙	Add a period
ℓ	Take out
⌒⌒	Move
☰	Capital letter
/	Small letter
¶	Indent

Now proofread your description of a movie scene. Check your spelling, punctuation, and capitalization.

A Use the Dictionary: Definitions

Here's a dictionary entry for the word *runner*. Notice that this entry has more than one meaning, and the definitions are listed by number. The most common use of the word is shown first.

run·ner /run ər/

1. *noun* Someone who runs in a race.

2. *noun* The long, narrow part of an object that enables it to move or slide, such as the blade on an ice skate or a sled.

3. *noun* A long, narrow carpet, often used on stairs.

Write a sentence for each dictionary definition of the word *runner*. Then read your sentences aloud to a partner.

_____

_____

_____

B Test Yourself

Each clue below refers to a place where a particular person or thing might be found. Decide which spelling word best fits the clue. Use each spelling word only once.

1. an unknown land
2. school building
3. college classroom
4. switchboard
5. book store
6. woodland trail
7. ship
8. kitchen
9. stage
10. hospital
11. greenhouse
12. track
13. bathroom
14. train
15. movie set
16. blood bank
17. watercolor class
18. living room
19. exhibit of statues
20. sewing shop

For Tomorrow...
Get ready to share the /ər/ words you found in magazines and newspapers. Remember to study for your test!

Get Word Wise

The word plumber comes from the Latin word plumbum, which means "lead." Long ago, Romans used lead pipes to carry water. Later, a person who repaired water pipes made of any material was called a plumber.

Word Study Strategy

See the word

Say it slowly

Link sounds and letters

Write

Check

END

Spelling Words

cleanliness
cloudiness
clumsiness
darkness
dizziness
drowsiness
fairness
fitness
forgiveness
gentleness
goodness
happiness
kindness
likeness
neatness
sadness
sickness
softness
weakness
wilderness *LOOKOUT WORD*

Review	Challenge
sculptor	awareness
nuisance	emptiness
cloudy	

My Words

_____

_____

_____

Learn and Spell

Suffix -ness

Ⓐ See and Say

> **The Spelling Concept**
>
> good (adjective) + -ness (suffix) = goodness (noun)
> forgive (verb) + -ness (suffix) = forgiveness (noun)
> cleanly (adverb) + -ness (suffix) = cleanliness (noun)
>
> The suffix -ness can be added to many words to form nouns. If the word ends in y, the y changes to i when the suffix is added.

Remember the give in forgiveness.

MEMORY JOGGER

Ⓑ Link Sounds and Letters

Say each spelling word. Look for the suffix -ness in each word. Then use the spelling words to fill in a diagram like this one.

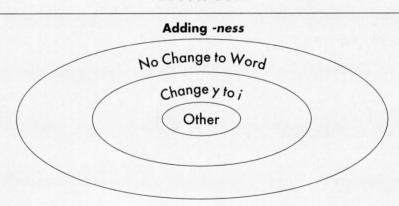

Word Sort

Adding -ness

No Change to Word

Change y to i

Other

Ⓒ Write and Check

The writer of this advertisement didn't quite finish it. Write another sentence for the ad. Use two spelling words in your sentence.

Fight <u>sickness</u> with
the <u>goodness</u> of nature!

_____

_____

Ⓐ Build Vocabulary: **Antonyms**

Antonyms are words that have opposite meanings. Write the spelling word that is an antonym for each underlined word.

1. not <u>hardness</u>, but _____

2. not the <u>city</u>, but the _____

3. not <u>dirtiness</u>, but _____

4. not a <u>difference</u>, but a _____

5. not <u>badness</u>, but _____

6. not <u>clearness</u>, but _____

7. not <u>health</u>, but _____

8. not <u>gracefulness</u>, but _____

9. not <u>cruelty</u>, but _____

10. not <u>happiness</u>, but _____

Ⓑ Word Study: **Suffixes**

The words in each pair below are formed from a base word and a suffix. Write the spelling word that is in the same word family as each pair.

11. neatly, neatest

12. fairer, fairly

13. gentlest, gently

14. weaken, weakly

15. dizzily, dizzier

16. darker, darken

17. fittest, fitter

18. happily, happiest

19. drowsing, drowsily

20. forgiving, forgiven

Spell Chat
Turn to the person next to you and challenge him or her to suggest four words formed from the word **sweet** and a suffix.

Be a Spelling Sleuth

You can see words ending with the suffix -ness in lots of advertisements. That's because advertisers often suggest that you can gain such qualities as happiness and fitness by using their products. Look for -ness words in magazine and newspaper ads.

Spelling Words

cleanliness	goodness
cloudiness	happiness
clumsiness	kindness
darkness	likeness
dizziness	neatness
drowsiness	sadness
fairness	sickness
fitness	softness
forgiveness	weakness
gentleness	wilderness

Review	Challenge
sculptor	awareness
nuisance	emptiness
cloudy	

My Words

_____

_____

_____

Spelling Words

cleanliness	goodness
cloudiness	happiness
clumsiness	kindness
darkness	likeness
dizziness	neatness
drowsiness	sadness
fairness	sickness
fitness	softness
forgiveness	weakness
gentleness	wilderness LOOKOUT WORD

Review	Challenge
sculptor	awareness
nuisance	emptiness
cloudy	

My Words

_____

_____

_____

Quick Write

Write two sentences about something unexpected that could happen. Use a word with the suffix *-ness* in each sentence. For example, *A rainbow suddenly appeared through the clouds, filling me with happiness.*

A Write a Narrative

 You may wish to do this activity on a computer.

Someone you know is on a hike when something unexpected takes place. Describe what happens. Include details about the setting and mood to make your writing come alive. Use the spelling words and other related words to zero in on the action.

B Proofread

Read Mei Lin's narrative. She made four spelling errors, two punctuation errors, and one capitalization error. Correct them.

Tip

When you write a possessive noun, don't forget the apostrophe!

> Janet hurried to reach camp before the cloudey sky turned to darknes. Suddenly, Janets dog bounded out of a thicket with a fawn by its side. with surprising gentlness, the dog played with the fawn. Just ahead, Janet spotted a doe. The fawn ran to its mother, Janet raced her dog to their wildeness camp.

PROOFREADING MARKS

- ∧ Add
- ⩘ Add a comma
- ⸌⸍ Add quotation marks
- ⊙ Add a period
- ℓ Take out
- ◯⌃ Move
- ≡ Capital letter
- / Small letter
- ¶ Indent

Now proofread your narrative. Check your spelling, punctuation, and capitalization. Pay close attention to your use of apostrophes in possessive nouns.

Ⓐ Use the Dictionary: **Homophones**

Homophones are words that are pronounced alike but have different meanings and spellings. For example, the spelling word *fairness* is formed from the base word *fair* and has a homophone, *fare*. Check these dictionary entries for their meanings.

fare /fâr/

1. noun The cost of traveling on a bus, subway, train, plane, etc. **2. verb** To get along. *How did they fare on their trip?*

fair /fâr/

1. adjective Reasonable and just, as in *fair treatment.* ▷ **noun** fairness ▷ **adverb** fairly **2. adjective** Neither good nor bad. *Greg is just a fair student.* ▷ **adverb** fairly **3. adjective** fair Weather that is clear and sunny. **4. noun** An outdoor show of farm products and animals, often with entertainment, amusements, and rides.

Now write a sentence that includes the words *fair* and *fare*. Exchange sentences with a partner and check each other's spellings.

Ⓑ Test Yourself

Write the spelling word formed from each base word below + *-ness.* You may need to add or change one or more letters before the suffix.

1. weak	**11.** soft
2. neat	**12.** sick
3. happy	**13.** like
4. gentle	**14.** kind
5. forgive	**15.** good
6. fit	**16.** clumsy
7. fair	**17.** cloudy
8. drowsy	**18.** sad
9. dizzy	**19.** clean + ly
10. dark	**20.** wild + er

For Tomorrow...
Get ready to share words with **-ness** that you discovered in magazines and newspapers. Remember to study for your test!

Get Word Wise

Dizzy is the adjective that describes someone experiencing dizziness, but it also has the slang meaning "silly." Strangely, the modern slang meaning is the original meaning. It comes from the Old English *dysig,* "silly."

Word Study Strategy

See the word

Say it slowly

Link sounds and letters

Write

Check

END

Spelling Words

action
addition
attraction
celebration
collection
conversation
correction
decoration
direction
election
information
instruction
invention
invitation
occupation *LOOKOUT WORD*
preparation
protection
selection
situation
suggestion

Review	Challenge
wilderness	complication
straight	multiplication
discussion	

My Words

_____

_____

_____

Suffix -tion

A See and Say

The Spelling Concept

Verb	+	-tion	=	Noun
collect				collection
add				addition
inform				information
prepare				preparation

The suffix -tion can be added to many verbs to form nouns. Verbs drop a letter, add a letter, or change a letter when -tion is added.

> Prepare to lose the *e* in preparation for this lesson.

MEMORY JOGGER

B Link Sounds and Letters

Say each spelling word. Listen for the suffix -tion in each word. Then sort the spelling words on a chart like the one below.

Word Sort

Making words with the suffix -tion		
Drop Letter(s)	Add a Letter	Change a Letter

C Write and Check

Complete this couplet with spelling words formed from the verbs shown.

elect   In Spellville they held an _____.

select   But there wasn't that good a _____.

Now write a couplet of your own, using two other spelling words.

_____

_____

Ⓐ Build Vocabulary: Rhyming

Can you complete each rhyme below? Write the spelling word that rhymes with the underlined word in each sentence. The first letter is given as a clue.

1. If you ask me a <u>question</u>, I'll make a s_____.
2. My leg is in <u>traction</u> and keeps me from a_____
3. We ate jam all <u>vacation</u>—what a sticky s_____.
4. The professor won't <u>mention</u> her secret i_____.
5. They painted the <u>station</u>, just for d_____.
6. On July 4, the <u>nation</u> holds a c_____.
7. Don't run in the e_____ if you can't take <u>rejection</u>.
8. I have no <u>objection</u> to your famous stamp c_____.
9. Here's a party i_____ for my puppy, a <u>dalmatian</u>!
10. I'll hold an <u>inspection</u> before making my s_____.

Ⓑ Word Study: Suffixes

The computer is on the blink! Every spelling word it prints has the wrong suffix. Write the correct spelling word with the suffix *-tion*.

11. prepared
12. correctable
13. informative
14. attractive
15. conversing
16. occupied
17. director
18. instructor
19. protected
20. adding

Spell Chat

Challenge the person next to you to choose a spelling word and use it in a rhyming sentence like the ones on this page.

Spelling Words

action	information
addition	instructions
attraction	invention
celebration	invitation
collection	occupation
conversation	preparation
correction	protection
decoration	selection
direction	situation
election	suggestion

Review	Challenge
wilderness	complication
straight	multiplication
discussion	

My Words

_____
_____
_____

Spelling Words

action	information
addition	instruction
attraction	invention
celebration	invitation
collection	occupation
conversation	preparation
correction	protection
decoration	selection
direction	situation
election	suggestion

Review	Challenge
wilderness	complication
straight	multiplication
discussion	

My Words

_____
_____
_____

Quick Write

Write the first few sentences of a paragraph explaining how to ride a bicycle. Include spelling words like instruction and protection that describe the bicycle or how to handle it.

A Write a How-To Paragraph

Try composing your how-to paragraph on a computer.

Write a paragraph entitled *How to Plan a Great Party*. Give clear instructions about the steps involved, so they can be easily followed. Use your spelling words and other related words in the how-to paragraph. Include some compound sentences.

B Proofread

Read Reynaldo's how-to paragraph. He made four spelling errors, one punctuation error, and one capitalization error. Correct them.

Tip
Be sure to use a comma before joining words such as *and* and *but* in a compound sentence.

> The key to giving a great party is careful planning and discusion. First, you should talk over your plans with your family and you should get their approval. Then, list each friend to whom you'll send an inviteation. Include many of your friends. they don't have to know each other. Next, decide what snacks you'll serve and who'll help with the preperation. Finally, choose music. Make your party the celebracion of the year!

PROOFREADING MARKS

∧	Add
⌄	Add a comma
∨∨	Add quotation marks
⊙	Add a period
ℓ	Take out
⌒	Move
≡	Capital letter
/	Small letter
¢	Indent

Now proofread your how-to paragraph.
Check your spelling, punctuation, and capitalization.

ⓐ Use the Dictionary: Entry With Two Definitions

Here's a dictionary entry for the word *direction*. When an entry word has more than one meaning, the different definitions are listed in order, according to how often they are used in the language.

di•rec•tion /di rek shən/

1. *noun* The way that someone or something is moving or pointing. *We traveled in the direction of the lake.* **2. *noun*** Guidance or supervision. *Luis learned to ski under the direction of a famous pro.*

Write a sentence for each dictionary definition of the word *direction*. Then read your sentences aloud to a partner.

ⓑ Test Yourself

Write the spelling word for each clue below.

1. things gathered together
2. the process of getting ready
3. the act of voting someone into office
4. something made for the first time
5. something magnetic or appealing
6. something pretty for a party
7. a job
8. the circumstances at a particular time
9. facts and knowledge
10. something you do

11. right or left
12. teaching
13. a happy ceremony
14. something extra
15. an offer
16. a recommendation or plan
17. safekeeping
18. a talk with others
19. a choice
20. a mistake that is fixed

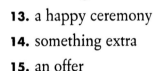

For Tomorrow...
Get ready to share your observations about words with the suffix *-tion* that you discovered. Remember to study for your test!

Get Word Wise
The word election, a word often associated with government, comes from the Latin word electus, which means "choice." In an election, we make a choice between two or more candidates.

Word Study Strategy

See the word

Say it slowly

Link sounds and letters

Write

Check

END

LESSON 11

Spelling Words

boredom
freedom
kingdom
stardom
wisdom *LOOKOUT WORD*
adulthood
childhood
neighborhood
argument *LOOKOUT WORD*
amazement
appointment
disappointment
enjoyment
excitement
government
statement
friendship
leadership
membership
ownership

Review	Challenge
occupation	embarrassment
peculiar	bewilderment
disappoint	

My Words

_____

_____

_____

Suffixes -dom, -hood, -ment, -ship

Ⓐ See and Say

The Spelling Concept

friend**ship**   the state of being friends
free**dom**   the state of being free
govern**ment**   the act of governing
child**hood**   the state of being a child

Words ending with the suffixes -dom, -hood, -ment, and -ship are nouns that usually refer to an act or a state of being.

Ⓑ Link Sounds and Letters

Say each spelling word. Look for the spelling of the suffixes -*dom*, -*hood*, -*ment*, and -*ship*. Sort the spelling words according to their suffixes. Then write the words in a chart like the one below.

> You can argue about it, but if you're wise, you'll always drop the *e* in argument and the *e* in wisdom.

MEMORY JOGGER

Word Sort

-ment words	-dom words	-ship words	-hood words

Ⓒ Write and Check

Make up a riddle like the one here for one of your spelling words.

_____

_____

_____

_____

RIDDLE

What kind of ship can last a lifetime?

friendship

A Build Vocabulary: Word Families

Write the spelling word that belongs in the same family as each group of words below. Then circle the suffix.

1. governorship, governor, governess
2. appointed, appointee, reappoint
3. neighbors, neighboring, neighborly
4. childish, childlike, children
5. adult, adultlike, adultness
6. wise, wisecrack, unwise
7. starlight, stargazer, starfish
8. freehand, freely, freeway

Spell Chat

Challenge the person next to you to choose a spelling word and to suggest as many words as possible that belong to the same word family.

B Word Study: Suffixes

Can you solve the equations ? Look at each symbol below. Each stands for a different suffix. Add the suffix to the word meaning in the equation, and you'll discover a spelling word. Write the word.

-dom = □   -ment = ○   -ship = ▽

9. stir up + ○ =
10. someone who has something + ▽ =
11. say + ○ =
12. disagree + ○ =
13. dull person + □ =
14. surprise + ○ =
15. someone who belongs + ▽ =
16. have fun + ○ =
17. someone in charge + ▽ =
18. someone you like and know well + ▽ =
19. let down someone + ○ =
20. royal ruler + □ =

Be a Spelling Sleuth

Look for examples of -dom, -hood, -ment, and -ship words in a book you are reading or other books at home. List the words you find.

Spelling Words

boredom	appointment
freedom	disappointment
kingdom	enjoyment
stardom	excitement
wisdom *LOOKOUT WORD*	government
adulthood	statement
childhood	friendship
neighborhood	leadership
argument *LOOKOUT WORD*	membership
amazement	ownership

Review	Challenge
occupation	embarrassment
peculiar	bewilderment
disappoint	

My Words

_____
_____
_____

Spelling Words

boredom	appointment
freedom	disappointment
kingdom	enjoyment
stardom	excitement
wisdom *LOOKOUT WORD*	government
adulthood	statement
childhood	friendship
neighborhood	leadership
argument *LOOKOUT WORD*	membership
amazement	ownership

Review	Challenge
occupation	embarrassment
peculiar	bewilderment
disappoint	

My Words

_____
_____
_____

Quick Write

Write two or three quick notes about a school event. You can write your ideas in short phrases. Include some spelling words in your notes.

A Write a News Article

You may wish to do this activity on a computer.

You are a reporter for your class newspaper. Write a short news article about an exciting school event. Don't forget to include the reporter's five Ws: *who, what, where, when,* and *why.* Make sure that the subjects and verbs in your sentences agree. Use some spelling words in your news article.

B Proofread

Read Randy's article. He made four spelling errors, one grammar error, one punctuation error, and one capitalization error. Correct them.

Tip
A subject must agree with its verb in number. Write **they are** and **she is** not **she are** and **they is.**

The La Playa Middle School supported Anns recent bid for the leadership of our student governement. many people knew Ann were destined for stardon. Her decision not to hand out buttons and flyers because of possible littering is typical of how she thinks ahead. Ann's ocupation one day might be in politics.

PROOFREADING MARKS

∧ Add
⌅ Add a comma
⌄⌄ Add quotation marks
⊙ Add a period
ℓ Take out
⌒ Move
≡ Capital letter
／ Small letter
¶ Indent

Now proofread your news article. Check your spelling, grammar, punctuation, and capitalization.

A. Use the Dictionary: **Word Endings**

The dictionary often provides related forms of a word at the beginning or end of an entry. These words often come after the word's part of speech.

a•maze /ə māz/

1. *verb* To make someone feel very surprised.
▷ amazing, amazed 2. *noun* amazement.
3. *adjective* amazing. 4. *adverb* amazingly.

Here's an entry for the word *amaze*. Look for its related forms. Then complete each sentence with a form of the word *amaze*. Next to the sentence, write the name of the part of speech of that word.

Wow! That rainbow is _____. _____

John performed _____ well on his spelling test. _____

B. Test Yourself

Complete each spelling word with the suffix *-dom, -hood, -ment,* or *-ship*. You may need to drop a silent *e* before adding the suffix.

1. enjoy + _____
2. child + _____
3. owner + _____
4. state + _____
5. appoint + _____
6. adult + _____
7. bore + _____
8. star + _____
9. disappoint + _____
10. leader + _____
11. govern + _____
12. wise + _____
13. king + _____
14. neighbor + _____
15. free + _____
16. member + _____
17. excite + _____
18. amaze + _____
19. argue + _____
20. friend + _____

For Tomorrow...
Get ready to share the words with the suffixes -dom, -hood, -ment, and -ship that you discovered in books. Remember to study for the test!

Get Word Wise

When is a suffix not a suffix? Think of the slang term *'hood. 'Hood* is a shortened form of the word neighborhood. The suffix -hood has come to stand for the whole word. *'Hood* may be the only example in American English of a word that was shortened by dropping everything but the suffix.

Word Study Strategy

See the word

Say it slowly

Link sounds and letters

Write

Check

END

The Cyclist Who CONQUERED ALASKA

Complete each paragraph with spelling words.

numeral	idol	wilderness
bicycle	explorer	

Jack had always dreamed of exploring faraway places. Sir Edmund Hillary, the first man to climb Mount Everest, was his __(1)__. Jack wanted to be an __(2)__, too. Like Hillary, he wanted the __(3)__ one beside his name. Recently, he had become interested in mountain biking. He had bought himself the best __(4)__ he could afford and was training for a trip in the __(5)__ of Alaska.

conversation	information	instruction	occupation
preparation	situation	wisdom	

Jack knew that careful __(6)__ was important to becoming successful. He gathered all the __(7)__ he could about Alaska. He had a long __(8)__ with a man whose __(9)__ was fixing bicycles. The man gave Jack some __(10)__ on how to make emergency repairs. The man also gave Jack the benefit of his __(11)__ from his own trips. He trained himself to deal with any __(12)__ that might arise.

novel	disappointment	refrigerator	icicle
author	cloudiness	happiness	radiator

The day Jack began his journey, the sky was cloudy, but a little __(13)__ couldn't stop him. He packed some food and a __(14)__ to read. He felt only __(15)__ as he started off. Soon, however, the temperature dropped, and Jack felt as if he were inside a __(16)__. He wished he were at home by the warm __(17)__. Even as an __(18)__ formed on his freezing nose, he thought about how Edmund Hillary had probably also felt some __(19)__. Jack pressed on, and today he is known as the __(20)__ of The Cyclist Who Conquered Alaska.

Good, Bad, or Indifferent?

Words that end with -*ness* often refer to a quality or a state of being. Among the states of being listed below, which would you most – and least – like to experience? Write them in order, with number one being the most desirable and number eight being the least desirable.

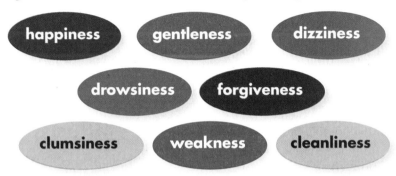

happiness gentleness dizziness

drowsiness forgiveness

clumsiness weakness cleanliness

Most Desirable

1. _____
2. _____
3. _____
4. _____
5. _____
6. _____
7. _____
8. _____

Least Desirable

Help Wanted

Fill in each "Help Wanted" ad with the spelling word that is the correct job title.

| author | director | explorer | janitor |
| conductor | operator | professor | sculptor |

9. _____
Must have repairing and cleaning skills to serve this office building.

10. _____
Teacher of history needed at Woodhaven Community College.

11. _____
Writer of mystery novels and short stories wanted.

12. _____
Orchestra is in search of new leader.

13. _____
Someone to head up new film. Must know cameras.

14. _____
Skilled person needed to run heavy equipment.

15. _____
Carver needed to create statue for new library.

16. _____
Must lead wilderness exploration. Map reading skills required.

WORDS WITHIN WORDS

Several smaller words can be found within the spelling word *disappointment*. To find them, read each clue and write the word it means.

1. liquid from a tree _____

2. a dot _____

3. adult males _____

4. something to help heal a sore

    _____

5. to choose someone for a job

    _____

Character Questionnaire

Think about writing a story about a fifth grader. First of all, decide who this person is. What is he or she like? What does he or she do? To help you develop your character, answer the questions below. Include each underlined word in your answer.

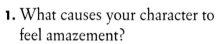

amazement

neighborhood

argument

ownership

appointment

government

disappointment   adulthood

celebration   example

boredom

1. What causes your character to feel <u>amazement</u>?

2. What does your character like most about the <u>neighborhood</u>?

3. How does your character feel during an <u>argument</u>?

4. If your character could have total <u>ownership</u> of only one thing, what would it be?

5. What kind of <u>appointment</u> would your character most want to be on time for?

6. What causes your character to feel <u>disappointment</u>?

7. What role would he or she play in student <u>government</u>?

8. What does your character think about <u>adulthood</u>?

9. What kind of <u>celebration</u> would your character plan for a friend's birthday?

10. What would cause your friend to feel <u>boredom</u>?

11. What kind of <u>example</u> would your character set for a younger person?

Look back at the words you misspelled on the Unit 2 Posttest and your My Words, Review Words, and Challenge Words. Proofread your writing for spelling, capitalization, grammar, and punctuation. Use the proofreading marks on this page.

Tip
Remember to capitalize the important words in all titles.

Sum It Up

Look back at your answers to the Character Questionnaire. Then write a short paragraph summarizing your character's qualities. Save your summary—you might use it to help you write your next story!

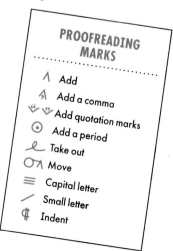

PROOFREADING MARKS

∧ Add

⋏ Add a comma

ᵛ⁄ ⱽ⁄ Add quotation marks

⊙ Add a period

ℓ Take out

↶↷ Move

≡ Capital letter

/ Small letter

ȼ Indent

Easily Confused Words

Read what Nick says. Choose the correct word to complete each sentence.

············· **principle   principal** ·············

1. Ms. Sanchez is the _____ of our school.

············· **election   selection** ·············

2. Carla said we will have a class _____ to choose students for the special events committee.

············· **collection   correction** ·············

3. We are going to plan the annual newspaper _____.

············· **decoration   direction** ·············

4. The officer received a _____ for her bravery.

············· **information   instruction** ·············

5. We signed up for swimming _____ .

············· **principle   principal** ·············

6. Holding elections is a _____ of a free society.

············· **idol   idle** ·············

7. Peter is always busy and never _____.

············· **conductor   director** ·············

8. The _____ led the choir in a song.

Nick says...

Some of my classmates were going on a wilderness walk, and I wanted to go, too. I left a note for my mom, asking her if I could. The problem was I wrote wildness instead of wilderness.

She wrote a note back saying I couldn't go do something wild, and we'd talk about it later. When she found out my spelling mistake she laughed, but I didn't!

Spelling Matters!

Learn and Spell

Spelling Words

admirable
affordable
changeable
comfortable
dependable
enjoyable
likable
livable
lovable
movable
readable
reasonable
remarkable
renewable
reusable
understandable
unforgettable ★LOOKOUT WORD★
unspeakable
unthinkable
washable

Review	Challenge
argument	believable
laughter	incredible
tremble	

My Words

_____
_____
_____

Learn and Spell

Suffix -able

A See and Say

The Spelling Concept

depend	-able	dependable
admire	-able	admirable
change	-able	changeable

The suffix *-able* means "capable of," "likely to," or "worthy of." Drop a final e before adding *-able* — except after a soft g.

B Link Sounds and Letters

Say each spelling word, and listen to the sound of *-able*. Place each word correctly on a diagram like the one below.

Don't forget the table in unforgettable.

MEMORY JOGGER

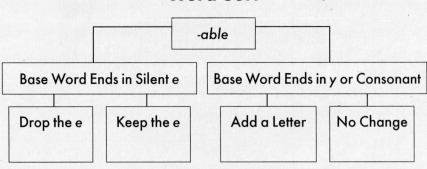

Word Sort

-able

Base Word Ends in Silent e → Drop the e | Keep the e

Base Word Ends in y or Consonant → Add a Letter | No Change

C Write and Check

Complete this ad for a sports car. Write the missing spelling words.

> If you like *comfort*, drive the most _____ car in the world. If you need a car you can *depend* on, here's the most _____ car in the universe. Meet Sprinter.

Now make up your own ad. Use three spelling words.

_____

_____

A Build Vocabulary: **Antonyms**

Antonyms are a pair of words with opposite meanings. *Un-* is a prefix that means "the opposite of." Read each word below. Then write the spelling word that is its antonym. Use the Spelling Dictionary if you need help.

1. undependable
2. unlikable
3. unremarkable
4. unchangeable
5. unwashable

B Word Study: **Suffixes**

Read each pair of sentences. Complete the second sentence with a spelling word.

6. We all *admire* Jason. He's an _____ young man.

7. Do you *understand* me? Am I _____?

8. Her kind words are a *comfort*. They make me feel _____.

9. Did you *enjoy* the show? Keisha found it _____.

10. Mary wants to *live* in a small town. She says small towns are very _____.

11. Don't you just *love* that kitten? It's so _____!

12. Don't *move* that desk. It's not _____.

13. I can't *read* your handwriting. It's not _____.

14. You can *reason* with Todd. He's a _____ person.

15. We want to *renew* our library books. They're _____.

16. Let's *reuse* that string bag. It's _____.

17. Our family can *afford* the apartment. It's _____.

Spell Chat

Challenge the person next to you to use words that end with the suffix *-able* to describe a person he or she admires.

C Write

Write a sentence using the words *unthinkable, unforgettable,* and *unspeakable*. For example, *How* unthinkable *and* unspeakable *to miss the* unforgettable *date of my birth!*

_____

_____

Be a Spelling Sleuth

Check out signs and newspaper want ads during the next few days. See how many words ending in *-able* you can find. Make a list. What do you notice about the way they're spelled?

Spelling Words

admirable	readable
affordable	reasonable
changeable	remarkable
comfortable	renewable
dependable	reusable
enjoyable	understandable
likable	unforgettable
livable	unspeakable
lovable	unthinkable
movable	washable

Review	Challenge
argument	believable
laughter	incredible
tremble	

My Words

_____

_____

_____

Spelling Words

admirable	readable
affordable	reasonable
changeable	remarkable
comfortable	renewable
dependable	reusable
enjoyable	understandable
likable	unforgettable LOOKOUT WORD
livable	unspeakable
lovable	unthinkable
movable	washable

Review	Challenge
argument	believable
laughter	incredible
tremble	

My Words

_____

_____

_____

Quick Write ✏️

Write two sentences about a favorite movie actor. Use a word with the suffix -able in each sentence. For example, *Andre is a completely unforgettable hero.*

A Write a Dialogue

You may wish to write your dialogue on a computer.

A student is having lunch with a favorite movie actor. Write a dialogue between these two characters. Include the title of the actor's latest movie, and capitalize the title correctly.

B Proofread

Read the beginning of Jana's dialogue. She made four spelling errors, one punctuation error, and one capitalization error. Correct them.

> **Tip**
>
> When creating an adjective with **-able** from a word that ends in a silent **e**, check the dictionary to see if the **e** is dropped.

"I just broke up with laghter at your latest movie, <u>The woman Who Does Everything Backward</u>," said Natalie. "We thought it was your most enjoyeable film yet."

"Thanks!" said the famous comedy actor, Michelle Mitchell. "I was a reasoneable person before I made that film? Even now, months later, I'm still doing things backward!"

Lunch was over, and she put her napkin on her lap.

"Remarkeable!" Natalie said.

PROOFREADING MARKS

∧	Add
⋏	Add a comma
⌄ ⌄	Add quotation marks
⊙	Add a period
ℓ	Take out
⟳	Move
≡	Capital letter
/	Small letter
¶	Indent

Now proofread your dialogue. Check your spelling, punctuation, and capitalization.

A Use the Dictionary: Syllabication

Here's a dictionary entry for the word *unthinkable*. Notice how the word is divided into syllables to help you with pronunciation.

un•think•a•ble /un **thing** kə bəl/ *adjective*
If something is **unthinkable**, it is out of the question.

How many syllables does the word *unthinkable* have? _____

The syllables for four spelling words are scrambled in the clouds. Unscramble the syllables. Then write the whole word.

ble•new•a•re

stand•ble•a•der•un

ford•af•ble•a

son•ble•a•rea

B Test Yourself

Read the definition. Then write the word that uses the suffix *-able*.

1. worthy of love
2. tending toward comfort
3. capable of being used again
4. worthy of being admired
5. cannot be spoken
6. can be washed
7. tending toward reason
8. can be enjoyed
9. able to be renewed
10. unworthy of thought
11. can be afforded
12. capable of change
13. worthy of being liked
14. worthy of being remarked on
15. likely not to be forgotten
16. able to depend upon
17. capable of being understood
18. worthy of being lived in
19. capable of being read
20. capable of moving

For Tomorrow...
Get ready to tell about the **-able** words you discovered on signs and in newspapers. Remember to study for your test!

Get Word Wise

The English word *depend* comes from the Latin *de-*, which means "down," and *pendere*, which means "to hang." The original meaning developed over time to mean "to rely on" or "to have support of," as if something hung down from and was supported by something else.

Word Study Strategy

See the word

Say it slowly

Link sounds and letters

Write

Check

END

Spelling Words

advance
balance
prance
entrance
allegiance *LOOKOUT WORD*
allowance
ambulance
appearance
assistance
attendance
circumstance
disappearance
disturbance
importance
silence
sentence
experience
innocence
confidence
intelligence

Review	Challenge
unforgettable	coincidence
principal	inheritance
elephant	

My Words

_____

_____

_____

Words With -ance and -ence

A See and Say

The Spelling Concept

-ance	allow	allow**ance**
-ence	sil	sil**ence**

Many words end with /əns/, a sound that can be spelled either -ance or -ence. If the ending is added to a verb that you recognize, it's often spelled -ance. Often the ending -ence and sometimes the ending -ance appear after word parts that cannot stand alone.

B Link Sounds and Letters

Say each spelling word. Look at the word ending. Write the words in the correct circle of a target.

My appearance matched my experience.

MEMORY JOGGER

Word Sort

-ance Words

-ence Words

C Write and Check

Write the spelling words that answer the questions.
What does a seesaw help you do? _ _ _ _ _ _ _

What's an antonym for *exit*? _ _ _ _ _ _ _ _

Now write a complete sentence using the word *intelligence*.

_____

_____

A Build Vocabulary: Related Words

Write a spelling word that is in the same word family as each word below.

1. advanced
2. prancing
3. enter
4. experiential
5. circumstantial
6. silent
7. innocent
8. confident
9. intelligent

Spell Chat
Pantomime an action that illustrates one of the spelling words. Have a partner guess the word.

B Word Study: Verbs to Nouns

You can form a noun by adding the suffix *-ance* to its related verb. Add *-ance* to each verb below to form a spelling word.

10. allow + _____ = _____

11. appear + _____ = _____

12. assist + _____ = _____

13. attend + _____ = _____

14. disappear + _____ = _____

15. disturb + _____ = _____

C Write

Write a short sentence for each of these spelling words: *importance, balance, sentence, allegiance,* and *ambulance.* For example: *Balance the dishes on the tray.*

_____

_____

_____

_____

_____

Spelling Words

advance	circumstance
balance	disappearance
prance	disturbance
entrance	importance
allegiance LOOKOUT WORD	silence
allowance	sentence
ambulance	experience
appearance	innocence
assistance	confidence
attendance	intelligence

Review	Challenge
unforgettable	coincidence
principal	inheritance
elephant	

My Words

_____

_____

_____

Write and Proofread

Spelling Words

advance	circumstance
balance	disappearance
prance	disturbance
entrance	importance
allegiance (LOOKOUT WORD)	silence
allowance	sentence
ambulance	experience
appearance	innocence
assistance	confidence
attendance	intelligence

Review	Challenge
unforgettable	coincidence
principal	inheritance
elephant	

My Words

____

____

____

A Write a Newspaper Column

You may wish to write your column on a computer.

Write a Safety Talk column for a local or school newspaper. First think of an emergency situation to write about. Then decide what steps should be followed if the emergency occurs. Use your spelling words and some imperative sentences.

B Proofread

Read the opening paragraph in Clyde's Safety Talk column. He made four spelling mistakes, two punctuation mistakes, and one capitalization mistake. Correct them.

Tip

When you write, be sure to use a period at the end of an imperative sentence.

Fires kill many people each year. Many deaths could be prevented if people just remembered three princepal rules. First, if you see smoke, get down on the floor? Next, before going through any entrence, check to see if the door is hot to the touch! Finally, if you have time, Call 911 and request assistence from the fire department. Firefighters have the expereince to help you escape safely.

PROOFREADING MARKS

- ∧ Add
- Add a comma
- Add quotation marks
- ⊙ Add a period
- Take out
- Move
- ≡ Capital letter
- / Small letter
- ¶ Indent

Now proofread your newspaper column. Check your spelling, punctuation, and capitalization.

Quick Write

Write two sentences about emergency situations that might occur at home or at school. Use as many words with -ence and -ance as you can.

A Use the Dictionary: **Stressed Syllables**

Here's the way the word *allegiance* appears in the dictionary. Notice the word's respelling between slashes. In words with two or more syllables one syllable is always stressed more than the others. In some dictionaries, an accent mark (´) shows the syllable that receives the stress. In other dictionaries, the stress is shown in boldface.

al•le•giance /ə lē jəns/ *noun*
Loyal support for someone or something.

Read aloud the respellings below, and listen for the stressed syllable. Tell where the stress belongs. Use the Spelling Dictionary if you need help.

/bal əns/ /in ə səns/

/ə ten dəns/ /sī ləns/

B Test Yourself

Complete each spelling word by using the code.

▽ = *ance*   ○ = *ence*

Yesterday's trial was quite an **(1)** experi○. Knowing its **(2)** import▽, we arrived two hours in **(3)** adv▽ of the trial. Reporters were everywhere, and we watched the senator **(4)** pr▽ past to avoid them, but then she lost her **(5)** bal▽ at the **(6)** entr▽ to the courthouse. We offered **(7)** assist▽, but the sound of **(8)** ambul▽ sirens soon broke the **(9)** sil○. Then the **(10)** appear▽ of the suspect caused another **(11)** disturb▽. The suspect's lawyer showed his **(12)** allegi▽ by describing the suspect's **(13)** confid○ and **(14)** intellig○. Even the lawyer made the **(15)** allow▽ that the **(16)** circumst▽ of the victim's **(17)** disappear▽ was strange. Still, he proclaimed the suspect's **(18)** innoc○ to everyone in **(19)** attend▽. Will there be a **(20)** sent○?

For Tomorrow...
Get ready to share what you've learned about words with *-ance* and *-ence*. Remember to study for your test!

Get Word Wise

The word ambulance comes from the Latin ambulere, which means "to walk." Think about it. Doesn't an ambulance do the walking for a sick or injured person?

Word Study Strategy

See the word

Say it slowly

Link sounds and letters

Write

Check

END

Spelling Words

alphabet
alphabetical
critic
critical
globe
global
history
historical
music
musical
occasion
occasional
office
official
ornament
ornamental
tribe
tribal
type
typical *LOOKOUT WORD*

Review	Challenge
allegiance	classic
explorer	classical
final	

My Words

_____
_____
_____

Suffix -al

A See and Say

The Spelling Concept

Noun		Adjective
critic	-al	critical
globe	-al	global
history	-al	historical

The suffix -al can be added to some nouns to form adjectives. Sometimes the spelling of the noun changes when -al is added. The silent e is dropped. Sometimes ic is added before -al. A final y is always changed to ic before adding -al.

> Remember to be log**ical** when you spell typ**ical**.

MEMORY JOGGER

B Link Sounds and Letters

Say each pair of related spelling words. Listen to the ending sounds of the noun. Do those sounds change when you add the suffix -al? Sort the pairs of spelling words into categories on a chart like the one below.

Word Sort

Add -al	Change final y to ic, add -al	Add ic before -al	Drop final e, add -al	Other

C Write and Check

Which spelling word can you find in the riddle? Write a riddle of your own using one or more of the spelling words.

_____
_____

RIDDLE

If all the letters of the alphabet were invited to a tea party, what letters would be late?

(The letters u, v, w, x, y, and z. They all come after T (tea).)

A Build Vocabulary: Multiple Meanings

Some nouns on your spelling list have multiple meanings. Use the noun that is needed twice to complete each sentence.

1. The candidate running for _____ announced that a campaign _____ would soon open in the neighborhood.

2. What _____ of _____ did you choose for the front page of our new school magazine?

3. People from around the _____ visited the model village and saw the beautiful crystal lamp _____.

B Word Study: Nouns and Adjectives

Some of the spelling words are nouns. They name people, places, and things. Other words are adjectives. They describe nouns. Use the clues below to write the spelling words.

4. Noun: a special event
5. Adjective: not often
6. Noun: a system of letters
7. Adjective: relating to a system of letters
8. Noun: study of the past
9. Adjective: relating to the study of the past
10. Noun: a song, for example
11. Adjective: relating to a song
12. Noun: decoration
13. Adjective: decorative
14. Noun: someone who finds fault
15. Adjective: finding fault
16. Noun: a group of people
17. Adjective: relating to a group
18. Adjective: approved
19. Adjective: characteristic
20. Adjective: relating to the world

Be a Spelling Sleuth

Look in entertainment and travel magazines for words with the suffix -al. Notice bulletin boards and posters too. Make a list of the words.

Spell Chat

With a partner, take turns suggesting new nouns and related adjectives with the suffix -al, such as comic/comical.

Spelling Words

alphabet	occasion
alphabetical	occasional
critic	office
critical	official
globe	ornament
global	ornamental
history	tribe
historical	tribal
music	type
musical	typical

LOOKOUT WORD

Review	Challenge
allegiance	classic
explorer	classical
final	

My Words

_____
_____
_____

Spelling Words

alphabet	occasion
alphabetical	occasional
critic	office
critical	official
globe	ornament
global	ornamental
history	tribe
historical	tribal
music	type
musical	typical

Review	Challenge
allegiance	classic
explorer	classical
final	

My Words

_____

_____

_____

Quick Write

Write three sentences that tell about a *typical* school day. Use as many related nouns and adjectives with the suffix -al as you can.

A Write a Third-Person Narrative

You may wish to write your story on a computer.

A third-person narrative is one that tells a story focused not on "I," or "you," but a *third* person—"he," "she," or "they." Write a paragraph in which you tell about a morning in the life of a student who lived 100 years ago. Write from the third-person point of view, using a name or *he, she,* or *they.*

B Proofread a Narrative

Read the opening of Tina's third-person narrative. She made four spelling errors, one capitalization error, and two punctuation errors. Correct them.

> **Tip**
> When you write a compound sentence, remember to use a comma before the conjunction.

For Tony Arroyo a typecal day began long before dawn. By sunup he had already fed the chickens and his brother José had milked the cow. Usually Tony and José just grabbed thick slices of bread before school but today was a historicle ocasion. José would take his finale school exam. To celebrate, Mama would make corn bread and bacon. the whole family would enjoy the special meal.

PROOFREADING MARKS

∧	Add
⋏	Add a comma
＂ ＂	Add quotation marks
⊙	Add a period
ℓ	Take out
↱	Move
≡	Capital letter
/	Small letter
¶	Indent

Now proofread your narrative. Check your spelling, punctuation, and capitalization.

Ⓐ Use the Dictionary: **Pronunciation**

Here is part of the dictionary entry for *critical*. Notice the respelling of the word following the entry word. The respelling tells you how to pronounce the word. The boldface syllable in the respelling shows the stressed syllable. Use the symbols in the Pronunciation Key in the Spelling Dictionary to help you pronounce the word.

crit·i·cal /**krit** i kəl/

Say each spelling word below. Then write the spelling word. Use the Pronunciation Key in the Spelling Dictionary to help you figure out the pronunciation symbols.

/**al** fə bet/ _____   /trīb/ _____

/al fə **bet** ə kəl/ _____   /trīb əl/ _____

Ⓑ Test Yourself

Write the spelling word that is hidden within each group of letters. Then write its related spelling word below it.

1-2.   m n a l p h a b e t q s v d
3-4.   p l c r i t i c a l w q
5-6.   i a d r z g l o b e p q
7-8.   a e z h i s t o r y m n a
9-10. z t p r s m u s i c a l a k v
11-12. t e o c c a s i o n v u r y x
13-14. p r o f f i c e a t t a h l
15-16. v q o r n a m e n t f y i b
17-18. c y q u t r i b e x h a n
19-20. o i a e g j t y p e u v

For Tomorrow...
Get ready to share the nouns and related adjectives with the suffix **-al** you found. Remember to study for your test!

Word Study Strategy

See the word

Say it slowly

Link sounds and letters

Write

Check

END

Spelling Words

courage
courageous *LOOKOUT WORD*
danger
dangerous
fame
famous
fury
furious
glory
glorious
humor
humorous
mystery
mysterious
nerve
nervous
outrage
outrageous
number
numerous

Review	Challenge
typical	joyous
cleanliness	continuous
beautiful	

My Words

_____
_____
_____

Suffix -ous

A See and Say

The Spelling Concept

danger	danger**ous**	No change to base word
nerve	nerv**ous**	Drop the final e
glory	glor**ious**	Change final y to i

The suffix -ous is added to many nouns to form adjectives. Sometimes a noun loses or changes a letter when the suffix is added.

B Link Sounds and Letters

Say each pair of related spelling words. Listen for the ending of the adjectives with the suffix -ous. Look at both words and notice any spelling changes. Then group the words in a chart like this one.

A final y may become a mysterious i.

MEMORY JOGGER

Word Sort

No Change to Base Word	Drop Final e	Change Final y to i	Other Words
Noun/Adjective	Noun/Adjective	Noun/Adjective	Noun/Adjective

C Write and Check

Answer these "moody" riddles with spelling words.

You twitch all over. When you speak, there is no sound. What is your mood? _ _ _ _ _ _ _

Nothing stops you. No one scares you. You are at your best. What is your mood? _ _ _ _ _ _ _ _ _

Now write your own mood riddle like the one above. The answer should be a spelling word with the suffix -ous.

Ⓐ Build Vocabulary: **Adjectives**

Adjectives describe people, places, and things. Notice that in each of the following sentences adjective and noun forms are underlined. For each underlined word, write a synonym from the spelling words.

1-2. The <u>beautiful</u> sunset made us wonder at the world's <u>beauty</u>.

3-4. What happened down at the creek is so <u>puzzling</u> that I might write a story called "The <u>Puzzle</u> at Hollow Creek."

5-6. If you're looking for <u>amusement</u>, get tickets to the very <u>amusing</u> "Mabel Mapleson's All-Star Revue."

7-8. If achieving <u>acclaim</u> causes you to lose privacy, who would want to be <u>well-known</u>?

Ⓑ Word Study: **Using Suffixes**

The suffix *-ous* means "full of, having, or possessing the qualities of." When an event is wond*rous* for example, it might be said to be "full of wonder." Use the word clues below to help you write the nouns and adjectives on your spelling list.

9. a noun meaning "shock"

10. an adjective meaning "having the qualities of a shock"

11. a noun meaning "a word used in counting"

12. an adjective meaning "having a large number"

13. a noun meaning "boldness"

14. an adjective meaning "having boldness"

15. a noun meaning "risk"

16. an adjective meaning "full of risk"

17. a noun meaning "anger"

18. an adjective meaning "full of anger"

19. a noun meaning "courage"

20. an adjective meaning "possessing no courage"

Spell Chat

With a partner, think of as many new nouns and related adjectives with the suffix *-ous* as you can. For example: adventurous, adventure.

Be a Spelling Sleuth

When you and your friends talk together or write notes to each other, you probably use adjectives such as outrageous and humorous to describe a situation or a mood. You might use a related noun, such as humor. Keep a list of adjectives and related nouns that you and your friends use.

Spelling Words

courage	humor
courageous	humorous
danger	mystery
dangerous	mysterious
fame	nerve
famous	nervous
fury	outrage
furious	outrageous
glory	number
glorious	numerous

Review	Challenge
typical	joyous
cleanliness	continuous
beautiful	

My Words

_____

_____

_____

Quick Write

Write two sentences for a journal entry about a weekend day. Use as many nouns and related adjectives with the suffix -ous as you can.

A Write a Journal Entry

 You may wish to write this journal activity on a computer.

What kind of day did you have? Was it incredible? Wonderful? Ordinary? Write about your day in a journal entry. Your entry can include real or made-up events along with details to describe them.

B Proofread

Usually, we don't formally proofread a journal, but sometimes we reread an entry and spot errors. Fernando made four spelling mistakes, two punctuation mistakes, and one grammar mistake. Correct Fernando's mistakes.

Tip
When you write two independent clauses in a sentence, use a comma before the **and**, **or**, or **but**.

What a humorus time I had at school today! It was anything but typicle. It started during math when Bill fell asleep and snored. Thought it was outrageous. Ms Suarez was furyous with all of us and we had to stay quiet for the rest of the class. Of course, that didn't help Bill. Into the silence came another one of his fameous loud snores!

PROOFREADING MARKS

∧	Add
⋏	Add a comma
⌄⌄	Add quotation marks
⊙	Add a period
ℓ	Take out
↶↷	Move
≡	Capital letter
/	Small letter
¢	Indent

Now reread your journal entry. Check your spelling, punctuation, capitalization, and grammar.

A Use the Dictionary:
Parts of Speech

For each entry word in a dictionary, you will find the word's part of speech: noun, verb, adjective, adverb, conjunction, preposition, or pronoun. The part of speech appears after the word's pronunciation.

Here are entries for the words *humor* and *humorous*.
Notice the parts of speech given in each entry.

hu•mor /hyo͞o-mər/
1. *noun* The funny or amusing aspect of something. **2. *noun*** A mood or state of mind.

hu•mor•ous /hyo͞o mər əs/ *adjective*
Funny, amusing.

Write the part of speech listed for each word.

humor: _____

humorous _____

Now write two movie titles. In one title, use the noun *humor*.
In the other, use the adjective *humorous*.

_____

_____

B Test Yourself

First write a spelling word that is a synonym for each of the following nouns. Then write the related adjective with the suffix *-ous*.

1–2. bravery
3–4. trouble
5–6. celebrity
7–8. anger
9–10. greatness
11–12. comedy
13–14. puzzle
15–16. courage
17–18. shock
19–20. count

For Tomorrow...
Get ready to share the nouns and the adjectives that describe moods. Remember to study for your test!

Get Word Wise

What do the meanings of the English words out and rage have to do with the meaning of outrage? Nothing, really. The word outrage is related to the French word outre and the Latin word ultra, both of which mean "beyond." What do you think someone goes beyond when he or she commits an act that is outrageous?

Word Study Strategy

See the word

Say it slowly

Link sounds and letters

Write

Check

END

Spelling Words

accident
accidental
accidentally *LOOKOUT WORD*
reside
resident
residential
honor
dishonor
honorable
dishonorable
honorably
science
scientist
scientific
unscientific
fortune
fortunate
misfortune
unfortunate
fortunately

Review	Challenge
courageous	disadvantage
instruction	advantageous
hopelessly	

My Words

_____
_____
_____

Word Building

A See and Say

The Spelling Concept

Base Word	Base Word and Prefix	Base Word and Suffix
honor	dishonor	honorable

Many words are built from the same base. Sometimes we add prefixes and suffixes to these words. Words with the same base are related in spelling and meaning.

After I ate my dinner, I received a fortunate fortune cookie.

MEMORY JOGGER

B Link Sounds and Letters

Say each group of related spelling words. Listen for the base word within each word. Then sort the spelling words on a chart like the one below.

Word Sort

Base Word	Base Word + Prefix	Base Word + Suffix	Base Word + Prefix and Suffix

C Write and Check

Can you say this tongue twister? Write your own tongue twister for one group of related spelling words.

_____
_____
_____
_____

TONGUE TWISTER
Fortunately, her fortune cookie did not foretell misfortune for the unfortunate.

Ⓐ Build Vocabulary: **Word Families**

Recognizing word families — or words that are related through a shared base word — will help give you spelling power. Look at the words on each balloon basket below. Then write the spelling words that are related to it.

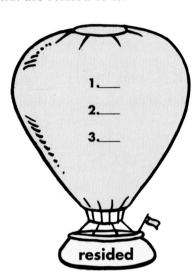

1. ___
2. ___
3. ___

resided

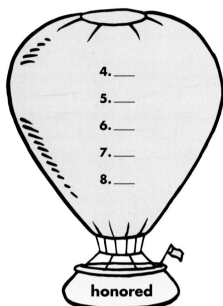

4. ___
5. ___
6. ___
7. ___
8. ___

honored

Ⓑ Word Study: **Parts of Speech**

Read each part of speech and definition below. Then write the spelling words they identify.

9. *adjective*; happening by chance

10. *noun*; something that is not planned

11. *adverb*; in a way that is not planned

12. *noun*; the study of the physical world

13. *adjective*; not having to do with science

14. *adjective*; having to do with science

15. *noun*; person who studies science

16. *adjective*; having to do with bad luck

17. *noun*; good luck

18. *noun*; bad luck

19. *adverb*; in a lucky way

20. *adjective*; having luck

Spell Chat

Turn to the person next to you, and say one word from a family of related words. Challenge him or her to say other words from that word family.

Spelling Words

accident	honorably
accidental	science
accidentally *LOOKOUT WORD*	scientist
reside	scientific
resident	unscientific
residential	fortune
honor	fortunate
dishonor	misfortune
honorable	unfortunate
dishonorable	fortunately

Review	Challenge
courageous	disadvantage
instruction	advantageous
hopelessly	

My Words

_____

_____

_____

Spelling Words

accident	honorably
accidental	science
accidentally 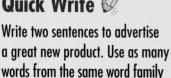	scientist
reside	scientific
resident	unscientific
residential	fortune
honor	fortunate
dishonor	misfortune
honorable	unfortunate
dishonorable	fortunately

Review	Challenge
courageous	disadvantage
instruction	advantageous
hopelessly	

My Words

_____

_____

_____

Quick Write

Write two sentences to advertise a great new product. Use as many words from the same word family as possible. For example, "Any scientist appreciates good scientific research."

A Write a Fictional Journal Entry

You may wish to do this activity on a computer.

Brainstorm a few scientific discoveries that could be helpful to human beings. Then imagine that you are the scientist who *accidentally* makes one of those discoveries. Write a journal entry telling about your discovery.

B Proofread

Read the opening paragraph of Sonya's journal entry. She made four spelling errors and two punctuation errors. Correct them.

Tip
Be sure to use a comma before the conjunction in a compound sentence.

> I am amazed by my discovery and thrilled at what it may mean for people everywhere. The other sceintist that I know is hoplessly jealous but she has not been as fortuneate as I have been in my laboratory. Everyone has congratulated me but I feel as though I deserve little credit. After all, discovering the anti-aging medicine was a complete accidint!

PROOFREADING MARKS

∧	Add
⋏	Add a comma
᭩᭩	Add quotation marks
⊙	Add a period
ℓ	Take out
◯↗	Move
≡	Capital letter
/	Small letter
¢	Indent

Now proofread your fictional journal entry. Check your spelling, punctuation, and capitalization.

A Use the Dictionary: **Example Sentences**

A dictionary entry often includes an example sentence in addition to a definition. From the example sentence, you can learn even more about a word's meaning. Here's an entry for *honor*.

hon•or /on ər/

1. *noun* Someone's *honor* is his or her good reputation. *She will ruin her honor if she fights for no reason.* **2. verb** To give praise or an award. *The mayor honored Kim for her bravery.*

Write an example sentence that uses *honor* to mean "to give praise or an award."

_____

_____

B Test Yourself

Supply the missing letters to make a spelling word. Write each word.

1. hon _ _ _ _ _ e
2. accident _ _
3. hono _ _ _ _ y
4. re _ _ _ _
5. _ _ scien _ _ _ _ _
6. _ _ _ hon _ _
7. hon _ _
8. resid _ _ _ _ _ _
9. accid _ _ _
10. _ _ _ hon _ _ _ _ _ _
11. accident _ _ _ _
12. sci _ _ _ _
13. for _ _ _ _
14. scien _ _ _ _ _
15. resid _ _ _

16. scien _ _ _ _
17. for _ _ _ _ _ _ _ _
18. _ _ _ for _ _ _ _
19. _ _ for _ _ _ _ _ _
20. for _ _ _ _ _ _

For Tomorrow...

Get ready to share related words that you found in advertisements, on posters, and on displays. Remember to study for the test!

Get Word Wise

The word science is related to the Latin word scire, which means "to know." What does the Latin word scire tell you about the words science and scientist?

Word Study Strategy

See the word

Say it slowly

Link sounds and letters

Write

Check

END

Underwater Adventure

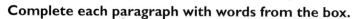

Complete each paragraph with words from the box.

> unforgettable   courageous   occasional   humorous
> occasion   fury   furious

Tomás and Lucia were having fun on their vacation. Except for an **(1)** thunderstorm, swimming in the Gulf of Mexico was great. Lucia was bold and **(2)** , and she had told Tomás that she wanted an **(3)** experience. Tomás was worried because Lucia was unpredictable. Although she did many **(4)** things, like sunbathing in a snowsuit, sometimes she went a bit too far. Tomás remembered the **(5)** of her tenth birthday, when Lucia almost swam out of his sight. Tomás became **(6)** . His **(7)** had a good effect, and for weeks afterward Lucia stayed nearby.

> misfortune   assistance   dependable
> accident   unthinkable

Tomás was the **(8)** , trustworthy one, and he would always come to Lucia's **(9)** in case of an **(10)** . Today, however, Tomás was in no mood for Lucia's **(11)** behavior. "We're not going to have any **(12)** and get hurt because of you!" he snapped.

> honorably   disappearance   ambulance   outrageous
> humor   alphabetical   intelligence   alphabet

"You're not going to have to call an **(13)** ," said Lucia. "I just want to have a little fun. While I'm underwater, we'll both slowly start saying the letters of the **(14)** in **(15)** order. Report my **(16)** to the lifeguard. Bring him here when you get to the letter s. Then I'll come up!" Tomás thought Lucia's plan was **(17)** .

"Use your **(18)** for a minute," he said. "While you're taking up that lifeguard's time, someone else could be in real trouble. Your idea of **(19)** is not funny."

Lucia had to admit Tomás was right. She told him, "I'll behave **(20)** , and I promise I'll never try such a prank."

Forming Nouns With -ance, -ence

Write the noun that is related to each word below.

1. appear _____

2. assist _____

3. disturb _____

4. innocent _____

5. intelligent _____

6. confident _____

7. disappear _____

8. ambulatory _____

9. circumstantial _____

disappearance   ambulance   appearance   circumstance   confidence   disturbance   intelligence   assistance   innocence

Doubly Describable

Write the -able spelling word that best describes both items in each pair.

admirable   comfortable   dependable
likable   livable   renewable   reusable

10. library books and video rentals _____

11. soft slippers and easy chairs _____

12. glass bottles and clean paper bags _____

13. good deeds and heroes _____

14. faithful dogs or best friends _____

15. farmhouses or cozy apartments _____

16. kind people and friendly pets _____

WORD PUZZLE

Complete the puzzle to find the description of someone most people probably wouldn't want to know. Write the words in the blanks.

a fury - y + ious, dis + honor + able, critical - al.

A _____, _____

_____

Now write your own puzzle (with spelling words) to describe someone you probably would want to know.

_____

_____

See It My Way

For each numbered item below, write a sentence about the situation. In your sentence, include the underlined word and one word from the sign at the left. Use each word from the sign only once.

Example: A <u>residential</u> neighborhood:

> *That* <u>type</u> *of sign can be found in a* <u>residential</u> *neighborhood.*

history   outrage

type   allegiance

courage   unspeakable

mystery

Tip
Remember to use a comma to separate the two clauses in a compound sentence.

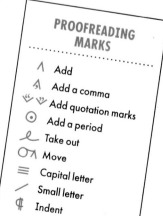

1. <u>humorous</u> situation: _____

_____

2. a <u>mysterious</u> situation: _____

_____

3. a <u>typical</u> situation: _____

_____

4. a <u>courageous</u> situation: _____

_____

5. an <u>outrageous</u> situation: _____

_____

6. a <u>critical</u> situation: _____

_____

7. a <u>historical</u> situation: _____

_____

Look back at the words you misspelled on your Unit 3 Posttests and My Words. Use them to describe another situation.

Tell About It

Select one of the situations above that is similar to one you've been in. Write a short account of this situation. Include some dialogue. Proofread your writing for spelling, capitalization, grammar, and punctuation.

PROOFREADING MARKS

∧ Add

⩚ Add a comma

ʬ ʬ Add quotation marks

⊙ Add a period

ℓ Take out

ↄ⁊ Move

≡ Capital letter

/ Small letter

¢ Indent

Building Words

Prefixes and suffixes can help you build different words in a word family. Write the right word from the ones in the box.

> **science**   **scientist**   **scientific**

Believe it or not, the _____ doesn't always

plan her _____ inventions. Many inventions in

_____ occur by chance.

> **accident**   **accidental**   **accidentally**

The process of strengthening rubber was invented by

_____. Charles Goodyear _____

dropped some rubber mixed with sulfur on a hot stove. The development

of strong rubber was purely _____.

> **misfortune**   **unfortunate**

This accident could have been _____ because,

at the time, Goodyear was a poor man who could not waste his

materials. However, Goodyear soon realized that instead of being a

_____, his accident was actually a lucky event.

> **dishonorable**   **honorably**

It is not _____ to come upon an invention by chance.

Goodyear did it, and so have others who _____

created inventions out of accidents.

Annie says...

If you're not careful when you're building words, you can build some that don't exist.

I once wrote the word *disfortunate* in a report. My friend, Keisha, thought the word was right, so she put *disunderstand* and *dispronounce* in her report.

When we gave our report to the class, they thought that *unfortunately* we both *disunderstood* *misunderstood* and *dispronounced* *mispronounce*.

What a mix-up!

Spelling Matters!

Spelling Words

taco
chili
mesa
plaza
salsa
fiesta
siesta
rodeo
patio
pinto
burro
burrito
mosquito
tamale
mustang
canyon
piñata LOOKOUT WORD
tortilla
llama
armadillo

Review	Challenge
accidentally	amigo
amazement	enchilada
tuna	

My Words

_____
_____
_____

Words From Spanish

Ⓐ See and Say

The Spelling Concept

Spanish	English
tortilla	tortilla
cañon	canyon

Many words we use in English come from Spanish. Some are exactly the same in both languages. Others may have a slightly different spelling or pronunciation. Notice that in the spelling word piñata the symbol ~ makes the letter *n* sound like the *ny* in canyon.

Ⓑ Link Sounds and Letters

Say each spelling word. Listen for the final vowel sound. Then write the words in the correct circle in a web like this one.

/l/ or /yə/ for double l? Practice so that you can tell.

MEMORY JOGGER

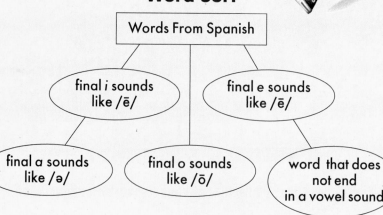

Word Sort

Words From Spanish

- final *i* sounds like /ē/
- final e sounds like /ē/
- final a sounds like /ə/
- final o sounds like /ō/
- word that does not end in a vowel sound

Ⓒ Write and Check

Read the following sentence: I ate a *taco* and a *burrito* out on the *patio*. Now write your own sentence, using at least two spelling words from Spanish.

_____

_____

Ⓐ Build Vocabulary: Classifying Words

Many of your spelling words can be classified by subject. Look at the spelling word list. Write words that are foods, places, and animals.

Foods

1. _____
2. _____
3. _____
4. _____
5. _____
6. _____

Places

7. _____
8. _____
9. _____
10. _____

Animals

11. _____
12. _____
13. _____
14. _____
15. _____
16. _____

Spell Chat

Challenge a classmate to describe an experience with one or more of the foods on the spelling list.

Ⓑ Word Study: Plural Nouns

Most words from Spanish are made plural by adding *s*. Write the spelling words below as plural nouns.

17. fiesta _____
18. piñata _____
19. rodeo _____
20. siesta _____

Be a Spelling Sleuth

Look for words from Spanish in stories you've read, mail-order catalogs, and at the supermarket. Where else might you find English words from Spanish?

Spelling Words

taco	burro
chili	burrito
mesa	mosquito
plaza	tamale
salsa	mustang
fiesta	canyon
siesta	piñata LOOKOUT WORD
rodeo	tortilla
patio	llama
pinto	armadillo

Review	Challenge
accidentally	amigo
amazement	enchilada
tuna	

My Words

_____
_____
_____

Spelling Words

taco	burro
chili	burrito
mesa	mosquito
plaza	tamale
salsa	mustang
fiesta	canyon
siesta	piñata *LOOKOUT WORD*
rodeo	tortilla
patio	llama
pinto	armadillo

Review	Challenge
accidentally	amigo
amazement	enchilada
tuna	

My Words

_____

_____

_____

Quick Write

Write three sentences describing a rodeo. Think about what sights, sounds, tastes, smells, and feelings you might observe there. Use as many words from Spanish as you can.

Write and Proofread

A Write a Description
You may wish to do this activity on a computer.

Think of some ideas for a fiction story in which the main character is a well-known chef of a Mexican restaurant. As part of the story, write a description of the restaurant. Include a description of several dishes that appear on the menu. Use some of your spelling words and some possessive nouns to describe the restaurant setting.

B Proofread

Read the description Alicia wrote of the restaurant setting. She made four spelling errors, two punctuation errors, and one capitalization error. Correct her mistakes.

Tip
Add **'s** to a singular noun to form a possessive noun. Example: the **boy's** hat.

> Walking into the Restaurant made me think immediately of my grandmas kitchen. To my amazment, bowls of colorful salza sat on every table. Platters of tamalis and burritos steamed on a nearby counter. The spicy scent of chilly filled the air. Sniffing hungrily, I imagined that I was in my families home again.

Now proofread your own description. Check your spelling, punctuation, and capitalization. Look for possible errors in the use of possessive nouns.

PROOFREADING MARKS

∧	Add
⋏	Add a comma
⌄⌄	Add quotation marks
⊙	Add a period
ℓ	Take out
⟲	Move
≡	Capital letter
/	Small letter
¢	Indent

Ⓐ Use the Dictionary: Etymology

Etymology is the history of a word. Many word histories are included in the dictionary. They may tell you the country or language where the word was first used or how the word came to have the meaning it has today. Read the word history for *rodeo* below.

ro•de•o /rō dē ō *or* rō dā ō/ *noun*

Word History Rodeo was first used to mean rounding up and counting cattle. It comes from the Spanish word **rodear,** which means "to surround." Only recently has **rodeo** come to mean an exhibition of roping and riding skills.

Use a dictionary to find another word history of a spelling word. See if you can find one for a word that comes from Spanish. In your own words, write what you find about the spelling word.

_____

_____

Ⓑ Test Yourself

Here is the list of spelling words for this lesson. Write the twenty words in alphabetical order. You may need to go to the second or third letter in a word to determine its order.

mustang	chili
tamale	plaza
burrito	burro
canyon	salsa
mesa	fiesta
piñata	mosquito
tortilla	pinto
llama	siesta
patio	rodeo
armadillo	taco

For Tomorrow...
Get ready to share the new words from Spanish that you found. Remember to study for your test!

Get Word Wise

Spanish explorers found many hills with steep sides and flat tops in the American Southwest. The explorers named these geographic features *mesas,* the Spanish word for "table."

Word Study Strategy

See the word

Say it slowly

Link sounds and letters

Write

Check

END

Spelling Words

active
activity
cruel
cruelty
curious
curiosity  *LOOKOUT WORD*
difficult
difficulty
dense
density
equal
equality
honest
honesty
loyal
loyalty
sincere
sincerity
special
specialty

Review	Challenge
piñata	enormous
dependable	enormity
thirsty	

My Words

_____

_____

_____

Suffixes -y, -ty, -ity

Ⓐ See and Say

The Spelling Concept

-y	honest	honesty
-ty	loyal	loyalty
-ity	sincere	sincerity

The suffixes -y, -ty and -ity are added to many adjectives to form nouns. Sometimes an adjective loses a letter when the suffix is added.

Ⓑ Link Sounds and Letters

Say each spelling word. Listen for the endings -y, -ty and -ity. Then sort the spelling words into three groups: adjective and related -y noun, adjective and related -ty noun, adjective and related -ity noun.

> It's curious that curiosity loses its u when -ity is added.
>
> MEMORY JOGGER

Word Sort

Adjective and -y Noun	Adjective and -ty Noun	Adjective and -ity Noun

Ⓒ Write and Check

Cats like to investigate everything!

What spelling word describes this trait? _ _ _ _ _ _ _

Change this word to complete a well-known saying:
"_ _ _ _ _ _ _ _ _ killed the cat."

Now write your own sentence about curiosity.

_____

_____

Ⓐ Build Vocabulary: Nouns and Adjectives

Help finish the pet guide below, and become a pet expert! Read each sentence. Then write the noun or adjective from your list of spelling words that would best complete each sentence.

1. Most puppies like to run and play. They are very _____.

2. When pets are sick they need _____ attention.

3. Salt water fish are _____ to keep in a fresh water aquarium.

4. Many people don't want to go through the _____ of keeping a salt water tank.

5. There are so many different kinds of pets today that some animal doctors have a _____ and treat only dogs or cats.

6. Some pets show more _____ to their owners than other pets.

7. Dogs are usually _____ to one owner.

8. Kittens can get into trouble because they are _____ and like to explore everything.

9. Kittens and puppies need a great deal of exercise and _____.

10. A pet that shows _____ about the world around it can be fun to watch.

Spell Chat
Turn to the person next to you and brainstorm three qualities important in a friend. Use words that end in -y, -ity and -ty.

Ⓑ Word Study: Adverbs

An adverb is usually formed by adding the suffix -*ly* to an adjective. An adverb that ends in -*ly* tells more about a verb, as in the sentence *Dan stared curiously at his sister's new pet.* Look at each adverb below. Write first its noun and then its adjective form. Remember, an adjective is a word that describes a person, place, or thing.

11–12. cruelly   **17–18.** honestly

13–14. densely   **19–20.** sincerely

15–16. equally

Spelling Words

active	equal
activity	equality
cruel	honest
cruelty	honesty
curious	loyal
curiosity	loyalty
difficult	sincere
difficulty	sincerity
dense	special
density	specialty

Review	Challenge
piñata	enormous
dependable	enormity
thirsty	

My Words

_____

_____

_____

Spelling Words

active	equal
activity	equality
cruel	honest
cruelty	honesty
curious	loyal
curiosity *LOOKOUT WORD*	loyalty
difficult	sincere
difficulty	sincerity
dense	special
density	specialty

Review	Challenge
piñata	enormous
dependable	enormity
thirsty	

My Words

_____

_____

_____

Quick Write

Write two sentences. Use related adjectives and nouns in each sentence. For example, *Loyalty is rewarded when others are loyal in return.*

A Write a Narrative

You may wish to write your story on a computer.

Write a short description of an event that could take place in a story about an animal who faces a problem. Set your story in nature or in a city. What kinds of problems might an animal face in either of those places? Use your spelling words and some contractions to make your writing interesting and descriptive.

B Proofread

Raul wrote a story set in nature. Correct the mistakes he made: four spelling errors, two punctuation errors, and one capitalization error.

Tip

When you form contractions, remember that an apostrophe replaces the letter or letters that you leave out when you combine the words: do not; don't.

The mother raccoon approached the small stream. Her babies followed with curiousity, their noses twitching theyd never been here before. They were thersty. Suddenly, their mother saw a fox. She needed to get her activ children to the other side. She nudged her loyel children onto her back, and she swam to the far bank. She knew the fox would not follow. Foxes hate water.

PROOFREADING MARKS

∧ Add

⅄ Add a comma

＂ ＂ Add quotation marks

⊙ Add a period

ℓ Take out

↻ Move

≡ Capital letter

／ Small letter

⊄ Indent

Now proofread your narrative. Check your spelling, capitalization, and punctuation.
Pay close attention to your use of apostrophes in contractions.

A Use the Dictionary: **Stressed Syllables**

Pronunciation respellings show you how to pronounce a word. They show you the sounds the letters stand for, and also which part of a word with two or more syllables should be said with greater stress. In the dictionary entries below, **boldface** type is used to show primary stress, and *italic* type to show secondary stress.

cu·ri·os·ity /*kyŏŏr* ē **os** i tē/
1. *noun* The desire to learn or find out.
2. *noun* Something odd that inspires interest.

curious /**kûr** ē əs/
1. *adjective* Eager to find out.
2. *adjective* Strange or unusual.

Study the respellings for the following pairs of words. Write the number 1, 2, 3, or 4 to show which syllable gets primary stress.

1. loy·al /**loi** əl/ ____

2. loy·al·ty /**loi** əl tē/ ____

3. e·qual /**e** kwəl/ ____

4. e·qual·i·ty /ē **kwäl** i tē/ ____

B Test Yourself

Write the two spelling words that are related to each word below. First write the adjective, and then write the noun.

1–2. act

3–4. curiosities

5–6. difficulties

7–8. especially

9–10. densely

11–12. sincerely

13–14. cruelest

15–16. equalize

17–18. loyally

19–20. honestly

For Tomorrow...
Make a list of the new words you discovered, and be ready to share it with your class. Remember to study for your test!

Get Word Wise
The word curious comes from the Latin curiosus, which means "careful." Back in the fourteenth century, curious had the same meaning we know today—eager to know. Many years later, another meaning for curious developed, as in curious creature, meaning "strange."

Word Study Strategy

See the word

Say it slowly

Link sounds and letters

Write

Check

END

Spelling Words

exact
exam
examine
excite
excuse — LOOKOUT WORD
exercise
exhaust
exist
exit
expand
expect
expedition
expensive
experiment
expert
explain
explode
expose
extra
extreme

Review	Challenge
curiosity	exhibition
experience	exaggeration
mixture	

My Words

_____

_____

_____

Words That Begin With ex-

A See and Say

The Spelling Concept

expand	spread or stretch out
exit	means of going out

The prefix ex-, added to a root or base word, usually means "out," "outside," or "out of." Knowing what the prefix ex- means can help you remember the meanings of words that begin with this prefix.

> Students explode out through the exit after an exam.

MEMORY JOGGER

B Link Sounds and Letters

Say each spelling word. Listen to the syllable that is stressed in each word. Then sort the spelling words on a chart like this one.

Word Sort

Stressed Syllable With ex-	Stressed Syllable Without ex-

C Write and Check

What is a short form of the word *examination*? _ _ _ _

Add *ine* to find out how to look at something closely. _ _ _ _ _ _ _

Take away the last five letters to find out how to start both of these words. _ _

Now you're an "*ex-*" expert!
Make up your own word puzzle for another *ex-* spelling word.

_____

_____

Ⓐ Build Vocabulary: Antonyms

Antonyms are words that mean the opposite or nearly the opposite of each other. Write the spelling word that is the antonym of each of these words. Use your Spelling Dictionary if you need help.

1. shrink
2. hide
3. cheap
4. beginner
5. bore
6. enter

Ⓑ Word Study: Adding ex-

You already know that *ex-* can be added to a word part to form a word. Read each item below. Write each complete word.

7. -cuse
8. -amine
9. -act
10. -pect
11. -treme
12. -plain
13. -ist
14. -plode
15. -am
16. -haust

Spell Chat
Work with a friend to create a paragraph using as many *ex-* words as you can.

Ⓒ Write

Write a sentence, using these spelling words: *exercise, extra, expedition, experiment.*

_____

_____

_____

_____

Be a Spelling Sleuth

Look for words that begin with ex-, such as exit and extra, as you travel around your community. Check out signs on public buildings.

Spelling Words

exact	expect
exam	expedition
examine	expensive
excite	experiment
excuse	expert
exercise	explain
exhaust	explode
exist	expose
exit	extra
expand	extreme

Review	Challenge
curiosity	exhibition
experience	exaggeration
mixture	

My Words

_____

_____

_____

Spelling Words

exact	expect
exam	expedition
examine	expensive
excite	experiment
excuse *LOOKOUT WORD*	expert
exercise	explain
exhaust	explode
exist	expose
exit	extra
expand	extreme

Review	Challenge
curiosity	exhibition
experience	exaggeration
mixture	

My Words

_____

_____

_____

Quick Write

Use as many words with ex- as you can to write a description of something that could happen on a mountain.

Write and Proofread

A Write a Journal Entry

You may wish to write your story on a computer.

You are leading a group of explorers on an expedition. Write a journal entry describing an experience you had. Brainstorm a list of words beginning with *ex-*, and include some of them in your writing.

B Proofread

Read this part of Jamie's journal entry. Find the mistakes he made: four spelling errors, two punctuation errors, and one capitalization error.

> **Tip**
> Always capitalize proper nouns, and remember that a direct quotation begins with a capital letter.

November 12

Before we go up the mountain, I will exsplain to the other explorers, "this expedition will exhaust you unless you are in excellent condition; To enjoy this expeerience, make sure that you are in extremely good shape. I exspect you to examin your equipment carefully. Pack exactly what you need and nothing more?"

Now proofread your journal entry. Check for spelling, punctuation, and capitalization errors.

PROOFREADING MARKS

∧	Add
⟨comma mark⟩	Add a comma
⟨quote marks⟩	Add quotation marks
⊙	Add a period
ℓ	Take out
⟳	Move
≡	Capital letter
/	Small letter
¶	Indent

Ⓐ Use the Dictionary: **Guide Words**

Guide words are shown on the top of each dictionary page. The first guide word shows you the first entry on that page. The second guide word shows you the last entry on the page. The other entries on the page come between the two guide words in alphabetical order.

exile ▶ exploration

ex•ile /eg zīl *or* ek sīl/ *verb*

To send someone away from his or her own country and order the person not to return. *The king was exiled from his homeland after the country was conquered by a new ruler.* ▷**exiling, exiled** ▷*noun* **exile**

Write ten spelling words that would be listed on the dictionary page between the guide words *exile* and *exploration*.

_____ _____ _____

_____ _____ _____

_____ _____ _____

_____

Ⓑ Test Yourself

Here is a list of spelling words for this lesson. Write the twenty words in alphabetical order. You will need to go to the third or fourth letter in a word to determine its order.

exact	extra
examine	exit
expand	explain
explode	experiment
exercise	exist
extreme	expedition
exam	excuse
exhaust	excite
expensive	expose
expect	expert

For Tomorrow...
Get ready to share the *ex-* words you discovered. Remember to study for your test!

Get Word Wise

Originally, to *exercise* meant "to let animals out." It comes from the prefix *ex-* ("out") and the Latin *arcere* ("to confine"). When the word was first applied to people, it meant "all worked up," as in "Don't get *exercised*." Today when we *exercise*, we are being active.

Word Study Strategy

See the word

Say it slowly

Link sounds and letters

Write

Check

END

LESSON
22

Spelling Words

port
porter
import
export
portable
portfolio
transport
transportation
report
reporter
motor
motion
motorcycle
motorboat
motorist
promote
promotion
remote
automobile
mobile *LOOKOUT WORD*

Review	Challenge
excuse	commotion
ornamental	emotional
adventure	

My Words

_____

_____

_____

Words With the Latin Root
port, mob, mot

Ⓐ See and Say

The Spelling Concept

Root	Meaning	Examples
port	carry	portable: able to be easily carried porter: one who carries
mot	move	motion: movement
mob		mobile: able to move

Many English words are built on roots that come from Latin. Sometimes we add prefixes, suffixes, or both. Words with the same root are related in spelling and in meaning.

Ⓑ Link Sounds and Letters

Say each spelling word. Look and listen for the Latin root. Then, on a chart like this one, sort the words by their Latin root.

You are able to move an object that is portable.

MEMORY JOGGER

Word Sort

port	mob	mot

Ⓒ Write and Check

What's a synonym for *car?* _ _ _ _ _ _ _ _ _ _

Which part of the word means "able to move"? _ _ _ _ _ _

What kind of home moves on wheels? a _ _ _ _ _ _ home

You moved in the right direction! Now use some of your spelling words to write a word puzzle of your own.

_____

_____

_____

A Build Vocabulary: **Roots**

Knowing the meaning of Latin roots will help you figure out the meaning of words containing those roots. Put the root meanings together with the clues below. Write the correct spelling word for each clue.

port = *carry*

1. person who carries
2. easily carried
3. person who brings news
4. flat carrying case

mob = *move*

5. vehicle that moves by the power of an engine
6. capable of moving

mot = *move*

7. heavy bike with an engine
8. boat with machine that makes it move
9. movement
10. machine that makes things move
11. far away
12. act of moving forward
13. someone who moves by car
14. move ahead

Spell Chat

With the person next to you, brainstorm a list of other words that have the roots port, mot, and mob, such as demotion.

B Word Study: **Prefixes and Suffixes**

Some of your spelling words are formed from combining the Latin root *port* with prefixes and suffixes. Look at the prefixes, suffixes, word parts, and root below. For each item, do the "math" and write the correct spelling word.

15. im + port =
16. ex + port =
17. trans + port =
18. trans + port + ation =
19. re + port =
20. transportation - trans - a - tion =

Be a Spelling Sleuth

Look for words with the Latin roots port, mob, and mot in newspaper and magazine advertisements, posters, and store signs. You may also want to look in sporting goods catalogs. Keep a list of the words you find.

Spelling Words

port	motor
porter	motion
import	motorcycle
export	motorboat
portable	motorist
portfolio	promote
transport	promotion
transportation	remote
report	automobile
reporter	mobile

Review	Challenge
excuse	commotion
ornamental	emotion
adventure	

My Words

_____

_____

_____

Spelling Words

port	motor
porter	motion
import	motorcycle
export	motorboat
portable	motorist
portfolio	promote
transport	promotion
transportation	remote
report	mobile
reporter	automobile

Review	Challenge
excuse	commotion
ornamental	emotional
adventure	

My Words

_____

_____

_____

Quick Write

Write four sentences, one of each type: declarative, imperative, interrogative, and exclamatory. Include at least one word with the root port, mob, or mot in each sentence.

Write and Proofread

A Write a Script

 You may wish to do this activity on a computer.

Write a scene for TV in which a talk-show host interviews an inventor. Use some of the spelling words.

B Proofread

Read this part of Kendra's script. She made four spelling errors, one punctuation error, and one capitalization error. Correct her mistakes.

> **Tip**
> Remember, a declarative sentence and an imperative sentence end in a period. An interrogative sentence ends in a question mark, and an exclamatory sentence ends in an exclamation mark.

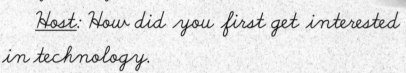

Host: Ms. Fixit, tell us about some of your inventions.

Ms. Fixit: Well, my most recent one is a solar-powered automoebil. it needs recharging only every 500 miles.

Host: How did you first get interested in technology.

Ms. Fixit: Technology is an advenure. I'm always searching for ways to create efficient means of transpertation. I think it's important that we make an energy-efficient moter.

Now proofread your script. Check for spelling, punctuation, and capitalization errors. Make sure you used each of the four kinds of sentences at least once.

PROOFREADING MARKS

∧	Add
⋏	Add a comma
＂＂	Add quotation marks
⊙	Add a period
ℓ	Take out
⟳	Move
≡	Capital letter
/	Small letter
¶	Indent

Ⓐ Use the Thesaurus: **Synonyms**

A thesaurus is an alphabetical book of synonyms. Many writers use a thesaurus to keep from repeating words in their writing. Related entry words, as shown in parentheses below, can lead you to even more word choices. Here is a thesaurus entry for *transport*.

trans•port 1. *verb* move, carry, conduct, ship (*See* **passage, transfer**)
2. *noun* movement, transit, shipment (*See* **passage, transfer**)

Write one sentence using the noun form of the word *transport*.

_____

Ⓑ Test Yourself

Write the spelling word that best completes each sentence.

1. If you _____ a product, you send it out of the country.

2. The TV news program will _____ on the crime.

3. The word _____ also stands alone as a Latin root.

4. Her job as a magazine _____ is to bring us political news.

5. The job of the _____ is to carry luggage to the hotel room.

6. Nina carries her _____ of writing and drawings to class.

7. Flatbed trucks _____ cars between states.

8. If you _____ a product, you bring it into a country.

9. Cars and trains are types of _____.

10. I can carry my _____ computer.

11. Design a poster to _____ good eating habits.

12. This car's _____ is running.

13. A flying airplane is in constant _____.

14. A _____ has two wheels.

15. That _____ home was moved from another city.

16. The _____ sped across the lake.

17. We celebrated when my mom got a _____ at work .

18. A _____ travels by car.

19. Use the _____ control to turn off the TV from here.

20. That red _____ is a good looking car.

For Tomorrow...
Be ready to share words you found with the Latin roots **port**, **mob**, and **mot**. Remember to study for your test!

Get Word Wise

Portus is the Latin root that means "to carry." When you **import** goods, you carry them in from a foreign country. When you **export** goods, you take them out. You **transport** goods by carrying them from one place to another. Something **important** is worth carrying.

Word Study Strategy

See the word

Say it slowly

Link sounds and letters

Write

Check

END

LESSON 23

Spelling Words

accept
except
affect
effect
farther
further
picture
pitcher
recent
resent
its
it's
finally
finely
formally
formerly
breath
breathe
decent
descent *LOOKOUT WORD*

Review	Challenge
mobile	envelop
mysterious	envelope
thorough	

My Words

_____

_____

_____

Often-Confused Words

A See and Say

The Spelling Concept

Often-Confused Words	Correct Usage
accept	I accept your apology.
except	We're all here except Ann.
its	The dog ate its dinner.
it's	It's a long time till dinner.

Many words in English look and sound almost alike. These words are often confused and used incorrectly in speech and writing. Be sure to think about the meaning of these words when you use them in a sentence.

Accept any answers except errors.

MEMORY JOGGER

B Link Sounds and Letters

Say each pair of often-confused words. Listen for the way each word is pronounced. Then sort the words on a chart like the one below.

Word Sort

Pairs With:			
Different Vowel Sounds	Different Consonant Sounds	Different Syllables Stressed	No Difference in Sounds

C Write and Check

Complete the word puzzle.

This word describes something that happened a little while ago. _ _ _ _ _ _ _ _

Drop the -ly to form a spelling word. _ _ _ _ _ _

Now write a spelling word puzzle, using one of the spelling words.

_____

_____

Vocabulary Practice

Ⓐ Build Vocabulary: Roots

Some words that are often confused have related roots. Use the roots and word meanings below to discover spelling words. Write the words. You may wish to use your Spelling Dictionary.

Root	Word Meaning
fec = make, do	1. a result
	2. to influence
breth = smell, exhale	3. to take in air
	4. air that is taken in
cept = take	5. to take something offered
	6. not including

Ⓑ Word Study: Confused Pairs

Read the passage below. Decide which word in each underlined pair correctly fits the sentence. Write the word.

Today, **(7)** its/it's class **(8)** picture/pitcher day. Everyone looks **(9)** decent/descent even though Josh's **(10)** resent/recent haircut was a disaster. His hair is sticking straight up in back.

The photographer wants the class to pose **(11)** formally/formerly. "Step back a little **(12)** further/farther," she tells the last row of students. Josh steps back too far and falls off the chair. His friends on both sides catch him on his **(13)** decent/descent. This is not Josh's day.

The photographer **(14)** finely/finally snaps the class photo. When Josh gets his copy of the photo, he is very happy. He's completely hidden behind Rosa's curly hair.

Ⓒ Write

Write at least three sentences with these words: *pitcher, resent, formerly, further, its, finely.* Underline the spelling words in your sentences.

_____

_____

_____

Be a Spelling Sleuth

Look for words that are often confused in magazine articles, newspaper stories, and fiction that you read.

Spelling Words	
accept	its
except	it's
affect	finally
effect	finely
farther	formally
further	formerly
picture	breath
pitcher	breathe
recent	decent
resent	descent

Review	Challenge
mobile	envelop
mysterious	envelope
thorough	

My Words

_____

_____

_____

Spell Chat

Talk with the person next to you about which words you often confuse. Suggest ways to remember them.

Spelling Words

accept	its
except	it's
affect	finally
effect	finely
farther	formally
further	formerly
picture	breath
pitcher	breathe
recent	decent
resent	descent **LOOKOUT WORD**

Review	Challenge
mobile	envelop
mysterious	envelope
thorough	

My Words

_____

_____

_____

Quick Write

Write two sentences, using recent and resent. Provide enough context clues to show that you know the difference between them.

A Write Idioms and Expressions

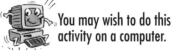 You may wish to do this activity on a computer.

"To catch your breath" is an idiom you may have heard before. Write an explanation of what this saying means. Then write an example sentence, using the idiom. Try to think of another idiom, and do the same.

B Proofread

Here are two entries from Carla's notebook for the expression "a picture is worth a thousand words" and "a breath of fresh air." She made four spelling errors, two punctuation errors, and one capitalization error. Correct them.

> **Tip**
> When you write a series of items in a sentence, use commas to separate each item.

A pitcher is worth a thousand words: This expression is not very mysterios. It's meaning is that a drawing diagram, or chart can often explain something better than a long written description A breathe of fresh air: This Expression has to do with a new or original idea.

PROOFREADING MARKS

∧	Add
⌄	Add a comma
⌄⌄	Add quotation marks
⊙	Add a period
ℓ	Take out
⌒	Move
≡	Capital letter
/	Small letter
¶	Indent

Now proofread your own writing. Check for errors in spelling, punctuation, and capitalization.

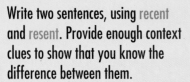

A Use the Dictionary: Pronunciation Key

All dictionaries have a key to help you figure out how to pronounce words.

Look at the pronunciation key below and the dictionary entries for *breath* and *breathe*.

breath /breth/ *noun*

The air you take into your lungs and breathe out again.

breathe /brēth/ *verb*

To take air in and out of your lungs.

Pronunciation Key	
/e/	end, wet
/ē/	even, see

Which word has the same vowel sound as in *met*? _____

Which word has the same vowel sound as in *beet*? _____

B Test Yourself

Use a pair of often-confused words to complete each sentence. For each item, write the correct word.

The steep ___(1)___ is not dangerous in ___(2)___ weather.

She will ___(3)___ all excuses, ___(4)___ Arturo's.

The ___(5)___ of a change in air pressure will ___(6)___ your ears.

He ___(7)___ introduced the woman who was ___(8)___ his teacher.

When he gets ___(9)___ along in his career, he'll move his office ___(10)___ from home.

Ask the ___(11)___ to sign this ___(12)___ of himself.

I ___(13)___ the ___(14)___ change in rules.

I think ___(15)___ odd that the dog chases ___(16)___ tail.

Geraldo ___(17)___ sliced the tomatoes as ___(18)___ as necessary.

Take a slow, deep ___(19)___, and you'll ___(20)___ more easily.

For Tomorrow...

Be ready to talk about the often-confused words that you found. Remember to study for your test!

Get Word Wise

The word resent first came from the French *ressentir* and *re* + Latin root *sentire*. Its original meaning was "to react" and was linked to *sense, sensation,* and *feeling.* Today resent relates to things that make you feel angry or irritated.

Word Study Strategy

See the word

Say it slowly

Link sounds and letters

Write

Check

END

Exploring the Grand Canyon

Complete each paragraph with spelling words.

mobile	exercise	expedition	experiment
expensive	exhaust	breathe	

Are you looking for an active vacation? Would you rather be **(1)** instead of sitting by a pool all day? Do you enjoy **(2)**, like walking and hiking? Do you want to **(3)** some clean, fresh air away from the car **(4)** of the city? Then **(5)** with an **(6)** your family will love. It's not as **(7)** as you might think.

canyon	armadillo	difficulty
extreme	transport	picture

Try to **(8)** yourself exploring the beautiful Grand Canyon. Although the trails are steep, a sure-footed mule will **(9)** you safely without too much **(10)**. The **(11)** beauty of the **(12)**, with its dramatic views, will amaze you. Along the trail, you might see interesting animals such as a spotted deer or a bony-plated **(13)**.

excuse	examine	exist	explain
transportation	remote	promotion	

Deep within the **(14)** reaches of the Grand Canyon, you might begin to think that this is where you want to **(15)** forever. You have no **(16)** not to treat yourself to this vacation. Take time to **(17)** our travel brochure, but then act quickly. This special **(18)** that we're advertising is for a limited time only. The package price does not include **(19)** to the Grand Canyon. Call and let one of our salespeople **(20)** the details.

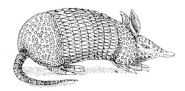

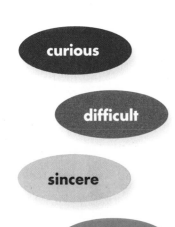

"Itty-Bitty" Word Changes

Write the spelling word that is a synonym for each word below. Then add -*ity* or -*y* to the word to turn it into a noun. Remember, you might need to drop a letter before making the noun.

curious

difficult

sincere

honest

dense

	Synonym	Related Noun
hard:	6. _____	7. _____
genuine:	8. _____	9. _____
truthful:	10. _____	11. _____
interested:	12. _____	13. _____
thick:	14. _____	15. _____

Move and Carry

Write the spelling word that finishes each sentence. Each sentence is about "moving and carrying."

portfolio   motorboat   motorcycle   automobile   portable

1. If you plan to carry a TV with you, it must be _____.

2. You can carry your writing assignments in a _____.

3. We'll take your books across the lake in our _____.

4. You'll get wet if you ride on a _____ in the rain.

5. We turned on the radio as we sped down the highway

   in our _____.

RHYME TIME

Read each clue. Then write the spelling word that rhymes with it. For example, a "Rhyme Time" for a "chubby lion" could be a *fat cat*.

pitcher   llama   siesta

1. A mother animal from South America

   _____ a mama

2. A baseball player who got a raise

   _____ a richer

3. A big party where everybody takes a nap

   a _____ fiesta

chili   canyon

pinto   piñata

burrito   tortilla

mosquito   armadillo

Are You Having Fun?

Congratulations! You're on vacation in Mexico and South America. You're keeping a journal of your trip. Write an entry about the experience. Use all the spelling words on the left as you tell about what you saw and did. **Tell about**

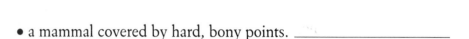

• a spotted wild horse you saw

  in a deep valley. _____

  _____

• a mammal covered by hard, bony points. _____

  _____

• a game you played at a birthday party in Mexico. _____

  _____

• an insect that stung you. _____

  _____

• three of the best dishes you have ever tasted. _____

  _____

Tip
Remember to use an apostrophe with contractions and possessive nouns.

Look back at the words you misspelled on your Unit 4 Posttests and My Words. Use some of them to write about another experience from your vacation.

_____

_____

Advertise It

Write a short, catchy advertisement to interest other people in a vacation like yours. Proofread it for spelling, capitalization, grammar, and punctuation.

PROOFREADING MARKS

∧ Add

⅄ Add a comma

ⱽ ⱽ Add quotation marks

⊙ Add a period

ℓ Take out

◌⌒ Move

≡ Capital letter

╱ Small letter

⊄ Indent

Often-Confused Words

Write the word that belongs in each blank. Be careful. The words in each pair are easily confused.

Sam says...

Uncle Ben wrote and asked me what I wanted for my birthday. I wrote back that I wanted a Bulls team pitcher.

When my present arrived, it was a Bulls mug with a note from Uncle Ben saying that he couldn't find a Bulls pitcher but a mug might be even more useful.

I guess I need to wait for next year, when I'll be sure to ask for the team p-i-c-t-u-r-e!

picture   pitcher

1. The baseball card had a _____ of a famous

_____.

formally   formerly

2. That teenager who is dressed so _____ today

_____ always wore jeans.

breath   breathe

3. When you have the hiccups, try to _____

regularly, but once in a while hold your _____.

recent   resent

4. Many people _____ the _____

changes in the hours that the music shop is open.

affect   effect

5. The changes in store hours that take _____ next

week will _____ many people.

Choose another pair of easily confused words from Lesson 23.
Write your own sentence, using both words.

_____

_____

Spelling Matters!

Changing Final y to i

Spelling Words

ability
abilities
enemy
enemies
victory
victories
liberty
liberties
berry
berries
diary
diaries
entry
entries
industry
industries
grocery
groceries *LOOKOUT WORD*
property
properties

Review	Challenge
descent	theory
honorably	theories
countries	

My Words

_____

_____

_____

A See and Say

The Spelling Concept

Singular	Plural
liberty	liberties
victory	victories

In many words ending in y, you form a plural by changing the final y to i and adding es.

B Link Sounds and Letters

When a singular word ends in a consonant and then a *y* pronounced /e/, you usually have to change the *y* to *i* and add *es* to get the plural /ez/. Sort the spelling words on a chart like this one.

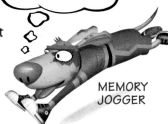

She cycles to the city for groceries.

MEMORY JOGGER

Word Sort

Singular Words	Plural Words

C Write and Check

Complete these sentences from a how-to book on self-improvement:

Put all your _ _ _ _ _ _ _ _ _ to work. They will lead you to _ _ _ _ _ _ _!

Now use two more spelling words to write your own one or two sentences for a how-to book.

_____

_____

A Build Vocabulary: Sentence Clues

You can unlock a word's meaning by reading the words that surround it in a sentence. Complete each sentence with a spelling word.

1. Each day Chantelle wrote in her _____.

2. Joy and her sister picked _____ in the field.

3. Mr. Arnez works in the dairy section of a _____ store.

4. The Declaration of Independence states that all people have the right to _____ and the pursuit of happiness.

5. Sam is such a bully that he makes many _____.

6. Growing tulips and making cheese are two important _____ in Holland.

7. Daniel is talented in art, and he has other _____, too.

8. Open the door, and walk through the _____.

9. Our house is on wooded _____.

10. We celebrated our team's _____ tonight.

11. There is only one more ripe _____ left on the blackberry bush.

12. Shana won the bronze medal for her swimming _____.

13. The automobile _____ employs many people.

14. A fox is the _____ of smaller animals such as rabbits.

Spell Chat

Write plural forms of three singular nouns that end in **y**. Then trade with a partner. Read each other's words, and explain what they mean.

B Word Study: Word Families

Words in the same word family share a root or a base word. Look at each word family below. Then write the plural noun that belongs in that family.

15. victory, victorious

16. liberty, liberated

17. entry, entryway

18. property, propertied

19. diary, diarist

20. grocery, grocer

Be a Spelling Sleuth

When you walk through a shopping mall or thumb through a catalog or magazine, look for pairs of singular and plural nouns that follow the pattern of this lesson. For example, you might see *candy/candies* and *curry/curries*.

Spelling Words

ability	diary
abilities	diaries
enemy	entry
enemies	entries
victory	industry
victories	industries
liberty	grocery
liberties	groceries
berry	property
berries	properties

Review	Challenge
descent	theory
honorably	theories
countries	

My Words

_____

_____

_____

Spelling Words

ability	diary
abilities	diaries
enemy	entry
enemies	entries
victory	industry
victories	industries
liberty	grocery
liberties	groceries LOOKOUT WORD
berry	property
berries	properties

Review	Challenge
descent	theory
honorably	theories
countries	

My Words

_____

_____

_____

Quick Write

Jot down your ideas about the meaning of the word *liberty*. Try to use at least two other spelling words.

A Write a Journal Entry

 You may wish to write this journal entry on a computer.

Wow! You woke up yesterday and found yourself in a place you always wanted to see. Was it a city in another land, a beautiful beach, or a national park? Write a journal entry in which you describe what you did at your dream place. Use colorful adjectives and words in a series.

> **Tip**
> When you write words in a series, separate each word in the series with a comma. For example, "I like red, white, yellow, and green."

B Proofread

Read Rick's journal entry. He made four spelling errors, one punctuation error, and one capitalization error. Correct them.

January 11

I can't believe I'm here in Yellowstone national Park in the most beautiful winter weather! Yesterday I kept looking up at the snowy peaks towering above me. What a sense of libertie I felt! This majestic properti is filled with abundant wildlife such as bears, deer elk, and buffalo. On my descant down a big hill, I even saw a bear cub eating berrys. I had a fantastic day!

Now proofread your journal entry. Check your spelling, punctuation, and capitalization.

PROOFREADING MARKS

∧ Add

⅄ Add a comma

ⱽⱽ Add quotation marks

⊙ Add a period

ℓ Take out

↶ Move

≡ Capital letter

/ Small letter

¶ Indent

Ⓐ Use the Thesaurus: **Synonyms**

A thesaurus is a book of synonyms, words that mean the same or nearly the same as another word. It is usually organized in alphabetical order. Each entry gives the word's part of speech and several synonyms. The thesaurus entry also gives related entries for the word, shown in boldfaced type. Look at the thesaurus entry for *property*.

property
noun belongings, possessions. *See* **home.**
estate, ranch, grounds. *See* **lot.**

Which related entry would you use to find more synonyms to replace *property* as it is used in this sentence?

This house stood on our family's property for generations.

_____

Which synonym would best replace *property* in this sentence?

There are several fruit trees growing on the property around Ms. Daniel's house.

_____

Ⓑ Test Yourself

Complete each spelling word below. Add the letters to make either a singular word or a plural word. Write the entire word.

1. abilit— (*singular*)
2. libert— (*plural*)
3. entr— (*plural*)
4. industr—(*singular*)
5. propert—(*singular*)
6. grocer— (*plural*)
7. enem— (*singular*)
8. enem— (*plural*)
9. diar— (*plural*)
10. victor— (*singular*)
11. abilit— (*plural*)
12. berr— (*plural*)
13. propert—(*plural*)
14. libert— (*singular*)
15. grocer— (*singular*)
16. industr—(*plural*)
17. berr— (*singular*)
18. victor— (*plural*)
19. diar— (*singular*)
20. entr— (*singular*)

For Tomorrow...
Get ready to share your observations about final **y** changing to **i** words you found when you walked through a shopping mall or leafed through a catalog or magazine.

Word Study Strategy

See the word

Say it slowly

Link sounds and letters

Write

Check

END

LESSON 26

Spelling Words

distant LOOKOUT WORD
distance LOOKOUT WORD
present
presence
absent
absence
different
difference
brilliant
brilliance
excellent
excellence
ignorant
ignorance
fragrant
fragrance
dependent
dependence
independent
independence

Review	Challenge
camouflage	magnificent
mosquito	magnificence
nonsense	

My Words

_____
_____
_____

Related Words

A See and Say

The Spelling Concept

Adjective		Noun	
-ant	distant	-ance	distance
-ent	absent	-ence	absence

To form a noun from its related adjective, change -*ant* to -*ance*, and -*ent* to -*ence*.

B Link Sounds and Letters

Say each spelling word. Look at the word ending. Then decide whether the word is a noun or an adjective. Sort the words on a chart similar to the one below.

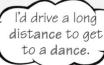

I'd drive a long distance to get to a dance.

MEMORY JOGGER

Word Sort

Adjectives With -*ant*	Nouns With -*ance*	Adjectives With -*ent*	Nouns With -*ence*

C Write and Check

What spelling words answer these riddles?

_____

Use the noun and adjective forms of one of your spelling words to write your own riddles.

_____

_____

_____

RIDDLES

I am an adjective. I mean the opposite of *present*. What am I?
absent

I am a noun. If I am out from school, my _absence_ will be felt.

A Build Vocabulary: **Antonyms**

Antonyms are words that have opposite meanings. Six pairs of your spelling words are antonyms. Read the clues. Write the spelling words that are antonym pairs.

1. here
2. not here
3. needing support
4. not needing support
5. the state of being in a place
6. the state of not being there
7. the state of needing support
8. the ability to rely on yourself
9. very smart
10. not aware of something
11. the state of being very smart
12. the state of being unaware

B Word Study: **Parts of Speech**

Adjectives describe people, places, things, and ideas. Nouns can name states of being or qualities. Read each part of speech and description. Then write the correct spelling word.

13. *noun;* the quality of being very good
14. *noun;* the state of being unlike
15. *adjective;* very good
16. *adjective;* having a pleasing smell
17. *adjective;* not alike
18. *noun;* a sweet smell
19. *noun;* space between things
20. *adjective;* far

Spell Chat

Work with a partner to come up with noun/adjective pairs that end in -ence/-ent or -ance/-ant. One partner should suggest a noun—for example, reliance—and the other partner can provide its adjective, reliant. Then reverse roles.

Be a Spelling Sleuth

Keep your eyes open for words that end in -ent/-ence and -ant/-ance. For starters, look in sports magazines and the sports section of the newspaper. Make a list of words you find.

Spelling Words

distant LOOKOUT WORD	excellent
distance LOOKOUT WORD	excellence
present	ignorant
presence	ignorance
absent	fragrant
absence	fragrance
different	dependent
difference	dependence
brilliant	independent
brilliance	independence

Review	Challenge
camouflage	magnificent
mosquito	magnificence
nonsense	

My Words

_____

_____

_____

Spelling Words

distant 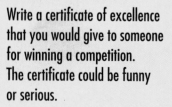	excellent
distance	excellence
present	ignorant
presence	ignorance
absent	fragrant
absence	fragrance
different	dependent
difference	dependence
brilliant	independent
brilliance	independence

Review	Challenge
camouflage	magnificent
mosquito	magnificence
nonsense	

My Words

_____

_____

_____

Quick Write

Write a certificate of excellence that you would give to someone for winning a competition. The certificate could be funny or serious.

A Write an Informative Paragraph

You may wish to do this activity on a computer.

You are a journalist reporting on a competition. It could be anything—from a school track meet to a national spelling bee. Choose something you know about, and write a paragraph reporting your observations.

B Proofread

Read this part of Randy's article. She made four spelling errors, two punctuation errors, and two capitalization errors. Correct them.

Tip

In pronoun contractions, such as I'll (I will) or she's (she is), an apostrophe takes the place of a missing letter or letters.

I always find it exciting to be presant at a live sports competition. last saturday I traveled to a distant city to watch the high school long-distence runners. Theyre my idea of excellant athletes. If I could camauflage myself, Id be on the track with them in a second. The athletic brilliance of this team is mind-boggling.

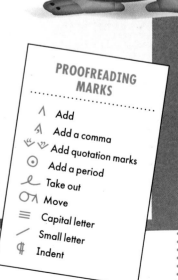

PROOFREADING MARKS

∧ Add

⅄ Add a comma

ᵥᵥ ᵥᵥ Add quotation marks

⊙ Add a period

ℓ Take out

⌒ Move

≡ Capital letter

／ Small letter

¶ Indent

Now proofread your own informative paragraph. Check for spelling, punctuation, and capitalization.

Ⓐ Use the Dictionary: **Homophones**

Homophones are words that sound alike but have different meanings and different spellings. One way to be sure that you are using the correct word is to check a dictionary.

---

pres·ence /prez əns/ *noun*
Being in a place at a certain time. *We would appreciate your presence at our party.*

pres·ent /prez ənt/ *noun*
Something that you give to someone, as in a *birthday present.* **plural** **presents**

In the entry above, *presence* and the plural *presents* are a pair of homophones. Write the homophone that belongs in each sentence below.

1. I got a pile of birthday ——————————— .

2. I was glad for your ———————————
when my dog was so sick.

Ⓑ Test Yourself

Look at the adjective and noun endings below. Pair them with the word parts to create the spelling words. Write each word.

-ance, -ence, -ant, -ent

1. fragr _ _ _
2. differ _ _ _
3. depend _ _ _
4. pres _ _ _ _
5. ignor _ _ _
6. differ _ _ _ _
7. brilli _ _ _ _
8. independ _ _ _
9. brilli _ _ _
10. excell _ _ _

11. fragr _ _ _ _
12. excell _ _ _ _
13. dist _ _ _
14. pres _ _ _
15. abs _ _ _ _
16. ignor _ _ _ _
17. dist _ _ _ _
18. depend _ _ _ _
19. abs _ _ _
20. independ _ _ _ _

For Tomorrow...
Be ready to share the related adjective/noun pairs that you discovered. Remember to study for the test!

Word Study Strategy

See the word

Say it slowly

Link sounds and letters

Write

Check

END

Spelling Words

dictionary
dictate
dictation
dictator
predict
prediction
contradict
contradiction
verdict
specimen   *LOOKOUT WORD*
inspect
inspector
inspection
respect
suspect
spectator
spectacles
spectacular
prospect
prospector

Review	Challenge
distance	speculation
specialty	perspective
question	

My Words

_____

_____

Words With the Latin Roots *dict, spec*

A See and Say

The Spelling Concept

dict	to speak	dictate	to speak aloud so someone can write down the words
spec	to look	inspect	to look closely

The Latin roots *dict* and *spec* (sometimes spelled *spect*) are used to build many English words. Prefixes and suffixes added to these roots create words that are related in spelling and meaning.

B Link Sounds and Letters

Say each spelling word. Look for the position of the Latin root *dict* or *spec(t)* in each word. Then sort the spelling words on a chart like this one.

The spectator wore spectacles to see the spectacular fireworks!

MEMORY JOGGER

Word Sort

dict__	__dict	__dict__	spec__	__spec__

C Write and Check

Complete the word puzzle.

Think of a synonym for *eyeglasses*. _ _ _ _ _ _ _ _ _ _

What's a shortened form of that word? _ _ _ _ _

Take away the plural ending to get a Latin root. _ _ _ _

Now write your own word puzzle, using a word with the Latin root *dict* or *spec(t)*.

_____

A Build Vocabulary: **Word Meanings**

Can you *predict* which spelling words with *dict* will match each definition? Write the spelling words to see if your predictions are correct.

1. to talk aloud so someone can write down what you say
2. a book of words
3. to say the opposite
4. a statement that is the opposite of what is being said
5. to say what you think will happen in the future
6. the decision of a jury
7. a ruler whose word is law
8. something that is said about the future
9. words that are spoken and recorded

Spell Chat

Ask the person next to you to suggest two words with the Latin root **spec** or **dict** that are not on your spelling list.

B Word Study: **Root Word**

Look at the *spec* root tree below. Use the clues on the branches to help you figure out your spelling words. Write each word.

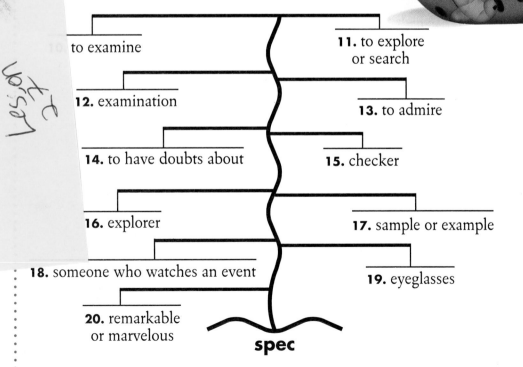

to examine

11. to explore or search

12. examination

13. to admire

14. to have doubts about

15. checker

16. explorer

17. sample or example

18. someone who watches an event

19. eyeglasses

20. remarkable or marvelous

spec

Be a Spelling Sleuth

Look for words with the Latin roots *dict* and *spec* on movie posters, signs, and other kinds of advertisements. For example, a movie poster might advertise *spectacular* special effects. Keep a list of the words you find.

Spelling Words

dictionary	inspect
dictate	inspector
dictation	inspection
dictator	respect
predict	suspect
prediction	spectator
contradict	spectacles
contradiction	spectacular
verdict	prospect
specimen	prospector

Review	Challenge
distance	speculation
specialty	perspective
question	

My Words

_____

_____

_____

Spelling Words

dictionary	inspect
dictate	inspector
dictation	inspection
dictator	respect
predict	suspect
prediction	spectator
contradict	spectacles
contradiction	spectacular
verdict	prospect
specimen	prospector

Review	Challenge
distance	speculation
specialty	perspective
question	

My Words

_____

_____

_____

Quick Write

Write two sentences. Use words with dict and spec(t) to describe something special that you've seen.

A Write a Job Description

 You may wish to do this activity on a computer.

Get ready to describe the career you've always wanted. It might be the job of a scientist, a detective, a lawyer, or a baseball player. You can find out about the career by reading about it or talking to someone who is in that profession. In your description, try to include a quote from that person.

B Proofread

Read Paula's job description. She made four spelling errors, two punctuation errors, and one capitalization error.

Tip
When you write direct quotes, use a comma to separate the quotation from the rest of the sentence.

When police are called to a crime scene, they sometimes bring a Detective. His or her job is to inspeck the scene for evidence left behind and queston the suspects. I look for footprints, strands of hair, and fingerprints" says one detective. "Then I can preedickt who might have done it. After the inspekshun, I usually write up a report."

PROOFREADING MARKS

∧	Add
⊹	Add a comma
⌄⌄	Add quotation marks
⊙	Add a period
℮	Take out
↶↷	Move
≡	Capital letter
/	Small letter
¶	Indent

Now proofread your description. Check for spelling, punctuation, and capitalization. Be sure you have used commas in quotations correctly.

Ⓐ Use the Dictionary: **Guide Words**

Guide words are at the top of each dictionary page. They show the first and last entry on that page. You can find words on that page that come alphabetically between the two guide words.

---

dictator ▶ digestion

dic•ta•tor /dik tā tər/ *noun*

Someone who has complete control of a country, often ruling it unjustly.
▷ *noun* **dictatorship**

---

di•ges•tion /dī jes chən/ *noun*

The process of breaking down food in the stomach and other organs so that it can be absorbed in the blood.

Look at the guide words on this dictionary page. Which words below would appear on the page? Write the words.

dictionary	dictate
contradict	difference

_____   _____

Ⓑ Test Yourself

Use the Latin roots below to help you figure out your spelling words. Write the words.

1. spec _ _ _ _

2. s _ spec _

3. _ _ _ _ _ _ dict

4. dict _ _ _ _ _

5. _ _ _ dict _ _ _

6. spec _ _ _ _ _

7. dict _ _ _

8. _ _ _ _ _ _ dict _ _ _

9. v _ _ dict

10. _ _ _ spec _

11. i _ spec _

12. spec _ _ _ _ _ _ _

13. _ _ spec _ _ _ _

14. _ _ _ spec _ _ _

15. dict _ _ _ _

16. _ _ _ dict

17. spec _ _ _ _ _ _

18. _ _ spec _ _ _

19. dict _ _ _ _ _ _

20. _ _ spec _

For Tomorrow...
Get ready to share the words you discovered on movie posters and in other locations. Remember to study for your test!

Get Word Wise

The spelling words with the root spec come from the Latin word spectare, "to watch," or specere, "to look at." A specimen is something you look at, spectacles are something you look through to improve your eyesight, and a spectator is someone who watches.

Word Study Strategy

See the word

Say it slowly

Link sounds and letters

Write

Check

END

LESSON 28

Spelling Words

bridle
bridal
patients
patience
tents
tense
scents
sense
assistance
assistants
instance
instants
stationary
stationery
bases
basis
muscles *LOOKOUT WORD*
mussels
currant
current

Review	Challenge
specimen	cymbal
expensive	symbol
bored	

My Words

_____

_____

_____

Other Homophones

A See and Say

The Spelling Concept

Homophone	Meaning
patients	people who are receiving medical treatment
patience	able to put up with hardship without complaint

Homophones are words that sound alike but have different meanings and spellings.

B Link Sounds and Letters

Say each homophone pair on your spelling list. Listen for the sound of schwa (/ə/) in each pair. Then sort your words on a chart similar to the one below. Use your Spelling Dictionary if you need help.

Don't get tense if the tents fall down!

MEMORY JOGGER

Word Sort

/əns/	/ənt/	/shə/	/əs/, /əl/	No /ə/

C Write and Check

Read the riddle. Then write the spelling words you found.

_____

Now use one or more spelling words to write a riddle of your own.

_____

_____

RIDDLE

What's the difference between a doctor who keeps her patients waiting and a doctor whose patients keep her waiting?

One needs patients with patience, the other needs patience with patients.

A Build Vocabulary: Context Clues

Here are two newspaper articles that need editing. Use context clues to fill in each blank with the correct homophone.

The __(1)__ reception for Amanda and Paul Blakely was held Saturday under two large __(2)__ . The __(3)__ of sweet-smelling flowers filled the air. __(4)__ and other types of seafood were served by waiters and their __(5)__ . This makes __(6)__ since both families live near the seashore. A __(7)__ -filled cake was served for dessert. The couple gave each guest personalized __(8)__ as a gift.

Horse riders understand the __(9)__ of having __(10)__ while training horses. They know that relying on the strength of their __(11)__ will not do the trick. For __(12)__ , the first time a horse wears a __(13)__ , it is likely to be unhappy. Trainers recommend that you keep the horse calm and __(14)__ . Be sure to get __(15)__ from someone who is experienced and not __(16)__ around large animals.

B Word Study: Meanings

Read the sentences to figure out the missing homophones. Write each missing homophone.

17. If you have *patience*, you can put up with problems without getting upset, but_____ are people who receive medical treatment.

18. An *instance* is an example or a specific case, but _____ are very short periods of time.

19. The _____ are the four corners of a baseball diamond, but the *basis* of a plan is the idea or reason behind it.

20. A *currant* is a small berry, but if something is _____, it belongs to the present time.

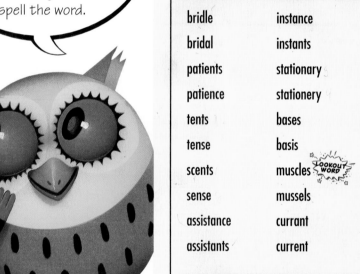

Be a Spelling Sleuth

Keep a list of sound-alike words that you hear on your favorite TV shows or see in store windows, such as *know* and *no*, *knew* and *new*, or *blew* and *blue*.

Spell Chat

With a partner, take turns drawing a picture to illustrate a spelling word and its meaning. See if the other person can guess and spell the word.

Spelling Words

bridle	instance
bridal	instants
patients	stationary
patience	stationery
tents	bases
tense	basis
scents	muscles
sense	mussels
assistance	currant
assistants	current

Review	Challenge
specimen	cymbal
expensive	symbol
bored	

My Words

_____
_____
_____

Spelling Words

bridle	instance
bridal	instants
patients	stationary
patience	stationery
tents	bases
tense	basis
scents	muscles
sense	mussels
assistance	currant
assistants	current

Review	Challenge
specimen	cymbal
expensive	symbol
bored	

My Words

_____

_____

_____

Quick Write

Write a funny sentence, using any pair of homophones on your spelling list.

A Write a Poem

You may wish to write your poem on a computer.

Did you ever see mussels with muscles? This line could be the beginning of a funny homophone poem. Use one or more pairs of homophones from the spelling list to write a short funny poem. It doesn't need to rhyme.

B Proofread

Read Lucy's poem. She made four spelling errors, one punctuation error, and one capitalization error. Correct her mistakes.

Tip

Remember, when writing a poem, be sure to use correct punctuation at the end of each line. It could be a comma, period, question mark, or exclamation point.

If You're Afraid

of Mosquitoes

if you're afraid of mosquitoes,
Wearing expensise scents
makes no sense.
Living in tense can
make you tents,
But building up resistance
is a great assistants

PROOFREADING MARKS

∧ Add
⋏ Add a comma
⤳⤳ Add quotation marks
⊙ Add a period
ℓ Take out
Ↄ∧ Move
≡ Capital letter
/ Small letter
¢ Indent

Now proofread your own homophone poem. Check for spelling, punctuation, and capitalization.

A Use the Dictionary: **Illustrations**

Dictionaries sometimes illustrate entry words to help you understand the words' meanings and to provide additional information. Look at the illustration for the entry word *muscle*. It is a labeled diagram. Use the diagram to answer the question below.

mus•cle /mus əl/ *noun*
One of the parts of your body that produces movement. Your muscles are attached to your skeleton and pull on your bones to make them move. *The diagram shows the muscles that move your arm.*

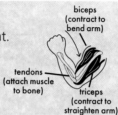

biceps (contract to bend arm)

tendons (attach muscle to bone)

triceps (contract to straighten arm)

In the diagram which two muscles are shown in black?

_____

B Test Yourself

Write the correct homophones to complete each sentence.

Someone who knows about perfume has the ___**(1)**___ to smell the ___**(2)**___ .

People who don't mind waiting for dentists are ___**(3)**___ with ___**(4)**___ .

If a horse could be in a wedding party, it might wear a ___**(5)**___ ___**(6)**___ .

A fresh new small fruit is a ___**(7)**___ ___**(8)**___ .

Writing paper that you hold still is ___**(9)**___ ___**(10)**___ .

If you're nervous about camping, you could be ___**(11)**___ in ___**(12)**___ .

If you need help from your helpers, you want ___**(13)**___ from ___**(14)**___ .

If ___**(15)**___ had ___**(16)**___ , they'd be very strong shellfish.

A baseball diamond shape is the ___**(17)**___ for the placement of the ___**(18)**___ .

Todd told me about an ___**(19)**___ in which all the lights went out for a few scary ___**(20)**___ .

For Tomorrow...
Get ready to share the other pairs of homophones you discovered. Remember to study for your test!

Get Word Wise

The word tense comes from the Latin root tensi or tent, meaning "to stretch." Originally, a tenter was a frame used to stretch cloth. If you are "on tenterhooks," you feel anxious. Even today, a tent is a piece of stretched cloth. When you are tense, you feel stretched, too.

Word Study Strategy

See the word

Say it slowly

Link sounds and letters

Write

Check

END

Words With the Latin Root sign

A See and Say

The Spelling Concept

re**sign**	to sign again; to give up a job
signal	marker that sends a message
de**sign**er	one who draws something to be made

Many English words are built on the Latin root *sign*, which means "mark." Sometimes we add prefixes, suffixes, or both to create new words.

B Link Sounds and Letters

Say each spelling word. Listen for the sound of the g in the root *sign* in each spelling word. Sometimes the g is silent. Then sort the spelling words on a chart like the one below.

What sign of significance should we design?

MEMORY JOGGER

Word Sort

Words With Silent g	Words With Sounded g

C Write and Check

Try saying this tongue twister three times—fast! Then write another tongue twister with *sign* words from the list.

_____

_____

_____

_____

TONGUE TWISTER

The designer will design the redesigned sign.

Ⓐ Build Vocabulary: **Synonyms**

Words with the same or almost the same meaning are called synonyms. Read each sentence below. Replace the underlined word with a spelling word that has almost the same meaning.

1. Many of Thomas Edison's inventions led to <u>important</u> changes in the way people live.

2. Very few people today would consider Edison's work to be <u>unimportant</u>.

3. The motion picture is one of Edison's discoveries that has great <u>importance</u> in our lives today.

4. Did you ever want to <u>plan</u> a special room just for you?

5. A good <u>planner</u> might observe you for a day or two before getting to work on your room.

6. If you are <u>planning</u> your own room, think carefully about what you most like to do.

Ⓑ Word Study: **Definitions**

Write the spelling word that fits each meaning below.

7. to give up an office or position

8. specific job given to somebody

9. pointing out or showing

10. giving up a job or position

11. to give somebody a specific job

12. giving somebody a specific job

13. replanned something

14. to give somebody a different job

15. symbol that stands for something

16. taking a job away from one person and giving it to another; assigning again

17. the way a person writes his or her name

18. message or warning

19. to make something known by speech or actions

20. gave up a job or position

Be a Spelling Sleuth

Look for words with the Latin root *sign* on school or computer bulletin boards, posters, or fliers. You might see a message such as this: "Sign up for a fabric design class."

Spell Chat

Turn to the person next to you, and brainstorm words with the Latin root *sign*. Include words with both the sounded and the silent *g*.

Spelling Words

sign	resigning
signal	design
signature	designer
significant	designing
insignificant	redesigned
significance	assign
signify	assigning
signifying	assignment
resign	reassign
resigned	reassigning

LOOKOUT WORD

Review	Challenge
muscles	signpost
portfolio	sign language
fashion	

My Words

_____

_____

_____

Spelling Words

sign	resigning
signal	design
signature	designer
significant	designing
insignificant	redesigned
significance *LOOKOUT WORD*	assign
signify	assigning
signifying	assignment
resign	reassign
resigned	reassigning

Review	Challenge
muscles	signpost
portfolio	sign language
fashion	

My Words

_____

_____

_____

Quick Write

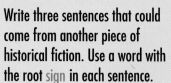

Write three sentences that could come from another piece of historical fiction. Use a word with the root sign in each sentence.

A Write Historical Fiction

You may wish to write your story on a computer.

It's July 4, 1776. You are sitting next to Thomas Jefferson and John Hancock at the signing of the Declaration of Independence. Write a paragraph that describes your impressions of the event. Use several words with the Latin root sign.

B Proofread

Read the paragraph that Geraldo wrote. He made four spelling errors, one punctuation error, one indenting error, and one capitalization error. Correct them.

Tip
Be sure to indent when you start a new paragraph.

The big room was silent in the sweltering summer heat the only sound came from some bees buzzing around a vase of flowers near an open window. A quill pen was handed to Mr. Hancock to sine the Declaration of Independence. As was his fashon, he signed slowly and with a flourish. People around him gasped. His sigiture was huge! Other names would appear insignficant beside Mr. Hancock's name.

PROOFREADING MARKS

∧	Add
⅋	Add a comma
ⱽⱽ	Add quotation marks
⊙	Add a period
ℓ	Take out
◠◠	Move
≡	Capital letter
/	Small letter
⌿	Indent

Now proofread your historical fiction. Check your spelling, punctuation, and capitalization. Be sure to indent.

A Use the Dictionary: **Example Sentences**

Dictionary entries show a word's pronunciation, part of speech, and different meanings. Entries may also include an example sentence to help you understand the different meanings of the entry word.

---

re•sign /rĭ zīn/ *verb*

1. To give up a job or position voluntarily. *I will resign from my job in May.*
2. If you *resign yourself* to something, you accept it without complaining. *She will resign herself to doing extra chores.*

Read the example sentences below for *resign*. Write 1 or 2, to show which sentence best fits each definition above.

1 Jack decided to *resign* from his job as captain of the chess team.

2 We will *resign* ourselves to giving up our holiday.

B Test Yourself

Use spelling words to complete the sentences below.

The __(1)__ boss tried to __(2)__ her trust in her staff.

The new building __(3)__ was made by the talented __(4)__ who spent years __(5)__ it.

Sandra is __(6)__ that she will __(7)__ from the student council. Her friend __(8)__ last month.

Ms. Torres did __(9)__ Joe as captain of the spelling team and wrote out the __(10)__ on the chalkboard. She had to __(11)__ it when Joe became sick.

Kevin thinks that television is the most __(12)__ invention of the century, but Nicole thinks it is __(13)__ compared with the __(14)__ of the computer.

Roberto's __(15)__ on the wall was a __(16)__ to __(17)__ his friends that he had arrived.

When the old movie house was __(18)__, I was responsible for __(19)__ many jobs.

The principal is __(20)__ all the teachers to new classes.

For Tomorrow...
Get ready to sign up and share the **sign** words you found. Remember to study for your test!

Get Word Wise

The word signature has different meanings. The meaning we use most often today is "a person's name written by himself or herself." In publishing, a signature means "a set of pages folded and gathered together for binding." The term *musical signature*, the key and meter of a piece of music, dates back to 1806.

Word Study Strategy

See the word

Say it slowly

Link sounds and letters

Write

Check

END

Good as Gold

Use spelling words to complete this script for a mystery play.

dictation	prediction	inspect
contradiction	assistance	brilliance

Inspector Ames: A priceless crown has been stolen. I'm going to __(1)__ the scene of the crime, and I'd like you to come with me. Bring your pad. I may need you to take some __(2)__ .

Mr. Smith: I'm happy to be of __(3)__ , Inspector. Will we be gone long?

Inspector Ames: It is my __(4)__ that this case will be solved very soon.

Mr. Smith: Knowing your __(5)__ , I will accept your opinion without __(6)__ .

victory	inspector	contradict
significant	assignment	

Inspector Ames: I'm certain the thief entered through this window. No one can __(7)__ me. Ask that officer to rope off the area. We may find __(8)__ clues here. I can smell __(9)__ !

Mr. Smith: I'll give her that __(10)__ immediately and tell her it comes straight from the __(11)__ .

spectator	distance	specimen
prospector	signature	

Inspector Ames: That man is not just a __(12)__ . I recognized him from a __(13)__ of at least 200 yards. He is John Doe, a famous gold __(14)__ . This __(15)__ of gold dust proves that he entered the house through this window to steal the crown. It is as good as a __(16)__ .

sense	patience	significance

Inspector Ames: Just as I thought! My __(17)__ has paid off. I've discovered something of __(18)__ . Common __(19)__ tells us this man is the thief.

Write It Right

Complete each sentence with the right homophone.

patience	patients	sense	scents
stationary	stationery	muscles	mussels

1. A veterinarian's _____ come in all different sizes.

2. You need kindness and _____ with animals.

3. Dogs notice _____ that people don't smell at all.

4. For dogs, the _____ of smell is important.

5. That restaurant serves shellfish known as _____.

6. The man lifting barbells has strong arm _____.

7. The desk is heavy; it's meant to be _____.

8. I buy letter-writing paper at the _____ store.

Synonyms

Read the adjectives below. Each one is a synonym for one of the spelling words. For each synonym, write the correct spelling word.

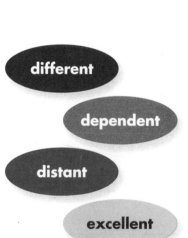

different
dependent
distant
excellent
absent
brilliant
present
independent

Adjectives	Synonym
faraway:	9. _____
missing:	10. _____
unlike:	11. _____
here:	12. _____
fine:	13. _____
helpless:	14. _____
self-reliant:	15. _____
shiny:	16. _____

WORD STEPS

Can you fill in this pyramid with words that start with *sens*? Add different suffixes to form new words. There is more than one correct answer.

S	E	N	S	E		

groceries   fragrant

mussels   stationery

brilliance   spectacular

dictionary   berries

spectacles   scents

signature   significant

Tip
You can form plurals of words that end in **y** by changing the **y** to **i** and adding **es**. For example: city/cities.

Catchy Ads!

A catchy ad can grab your interest. Do you think an advertisement for strawberries that says "Buy the Biggest, Juiciest Berries That Are Bursting With Flavor" would catch your interest? Think of some more catchy ads. Use at least two of the spelling words in each one.

BIG BERRIES FARM 1 MILE

1. for fruit _____

_____

_____

2. for seafood _____

_____

_____

3. for eyeglasses _____

_____

_____

4. for perfume _____

_____

_____

5. for writing paper _____

_____

Tell About It

Choose one of the products above. Write a complete advertisement for it. Describe all the reasons someone should buy the product. Proofread your advertisement for spelling, capitalization, grammar, and punctuation.

PROOFREADING MARKS

∧   Add

⋏   Add a comma

✌✌   Add quotation marks

⊙   Add a period

ℓ   Take out

Ↄ∧   Move

≡   Capital letter

/   Small letter

¢   Indent

John Doe, Guilty or Innocent?

The Latin root *dict* means "to speak." *Spec* means "to watch." Write the right word with a Latin root to complete each of these sentences about the gold thief, John Doe, whom you read about on page 124.

dictation	prediction	contradiction	verdict

1. What is your _____ —will John be found guilty or innocent?

2. The jury will come to a _____ after it hears both sides.

3. The judge will give _____ about the case to his secretary.

4. When one witness said the accused was in bed at 8:00, and another said he was at a party, they created a real _____!

spectator	spectacular	inspector
respect	specimen	

5. One _____ came to court every day just to watch the trial.

6. A police _____ by the name of Ames took the stand to talk about all the clues she'd found.

7. One _____ clue was the big fat thumb print.

8. When Ames told about John Doe leaving behind a

_____ of gold dust beneath the window, someone in the jury gasped.

9. The jury earned everyone's _____ when it delivered a just decision.

Kim says ...

Last week I turned in a social studies report about the California Gold Rush. I wrote, "One lucky spectator got rich for the rest of his life."

My teacher, Ms. Sanchez, wrote a note in the margin saying, "I wish I could get rich just from watching."

Later she told me I really meant to spell *prospector*— "one who searches for gold," not *spectator*—"one who watches."

Spelling Matters!

Spelling Words

kangaroo
pizza
menu
restaurant
café
spaghetti
moccasin
bouquet
zucchini *LOOKOUT WORD*
broccoli
ballet
piano
violin
beige
antique
cassette
crayon
yogurt
raccoon
karate

Review	Challenge
significance	mozzarella
further	boutique
hamburger	

My Words

_____

_____

_____

Words From Other Languages

A See and Say

The Spelling Concept

spaghetti	/spə get ē/	from Italian
bouquet	/bō kā/	from French
yogurt	/yō gərt/	from Turkish
moccasin	/mok ə sin/	from Algonquian
karate	/kə rä tē/	from Japanese

Our English language is rich in words from other languages. These words often have the same pronunciation and spelling in English as in their original language.

Chris likes to eat zucchini.

B Link Sounds and Letters

Say each spelling word. Listen for the numbers of syllables in each word to help you spell it. Then sort the words on a chart like this one.

MEMORY JOGGER

Word Sort

Words With 1 syllable	Words With 2 syllables	Words With 3 syllables

C Write and Check

Write the spelling words that answer the riddle.

_____ _____

Use at least two spelling words to write your own riddle like the one above.

_____

_____

RIDDLE
What's green and white and red all over?

a zucchini pizza

Ⓐ Build Vocabulary: **Analogies**

In an analogy, two pairs of words relate to each other in the same way. For example, *up* and *down* relate in the same way as *front* and *back*. (They are both opposites.) Write the spelling word that completes each analogy.

1. *Actor* is to *play* as *dancer* is to −.
2. *New* is to *modern* as *old* is to −.
3. *Circle* is to *shape* as − is to *color*.
4. *Paper* is to *cardboard* as *marker* is to −.
5. *Key* is to *piano* as *string* is to −.
6. *Soccer* is to *sports* as − is to *martial arts*.
7. *Hat* is to *baseball cap* as *shoe* is to −.
8. *Beef* is to *meat* as − is to *dairy*.

Ⓑ Word Study: **Plurals**

Most plurals end in *-s* or *-es*, like *violins* and *potatoes*. However, some words that end in *i*, like *broccoli*, are the same for both singular and plural. Read the meaning for the plural of each spelling word below. Write the word.

9. long, thin strands of pasta
10. small places where people eat light meals
11. vegetables in the squash family
12. large keyboard instruments
13. Australian animals with short front legs and long back legs
14. bunches of cut flowers
15. dining places that serve full meals
16. flat open pies spread with toppings
17. mammals with rings on their bushy tails
18. food lists used in places where people order meals
19. green, flower-like vegetables
20. flat, plastic boxes that hold recording tape

> **Spell Chat**
> With a partner, write four words that come from other languages. Tell what you know about their meaning.

Be a Spelling Sleuth

Look for words in cookbooks and on menus that come from other languages. Then take a tour of your supermarket to look at product labels. Keep a list of the words you find and where they came from.

Spelling Words

bouquet	antique
pizza	piano
kangaroo	violin
café	restaurant
ballet	yogurt
spaghetti	raccoon
beige	karate
cassette	moccasin
zucchini *LOOKOUT WORD*	menu
broccoli	crayon

Review	Challenge
significance	mozzarella
further	boutique
hamburger	

My Words

_____
_____
_____

Spelling Words

kangaroo	ballet
pizza	piano
menu	violin
restaurant	beige
café	antique
spaghetti	cassette
moccasin	crayon
bouquet	yogurt
zucchini *LOOKOUT WORD*	raccoon
broccoli	karate

Review	Challenge
significance	mozzarella
further	boutique
hamburger	

My Words

_____

_____

_____

Quick Write

Describe an animal that can do things animals can't do in the real world. Where does it live? What does it eat? Use at least two spelling words to write a sentence describing an animal in a fantasy story.

A **Write a Fantasy**   You may wish to write your story on a computer.

Many of the events that take place in a fantasy story could happen only in someone's imagination. Write an opening paragraph for a fantasy story. You could mix realistic details with imaginary settings. For example, your story could feature a ten-year-old boy who is the president of a club on another planet. Make sure to correctly place apostrophes in possessive nouns.

B **Proofread**

Read Jamal's paragraph from a fantasy story. He made four spelling errors, two punctuation errors, and one capitalization error. Correct them.

> **Tip**
> Remember to put an apostrophe in possessive nouns: Sal's bicycle; The car's motor.

Peter is the karaty master of the entire undersea world of Aquas. Carrying no weapons, Peter can defeat any enemy, ranging from a sharp-toothed shark to a swimming racoon who is batting its tail. Peters skill has earned him a lot of respect in aquas. He has earned furthur respect for his love of the arts. Once he has put down his enemies. he rushes off to dance with his friends in the underwater balet!

PROOFREADING MARKS

∧ Add
⩘ Add a comma
⹀ ⹀ Add quotation marks
⊙ Add a period
ℓ Take out
↻ Move
≡ Capital letter
/ Small letter
¶ Indent

Now proofread your fantasy writing. Check your spelling, punctuation, and grammar.

A Use the Dictionary: **Guide Words**

To find words in the dictionary quickly and easily, use the guide words at the top of each dictionary page. They show you the first and last words in alphabetical order found on that page. Which spelling word might be found on the page shown below? _____

bristle ▶ brother-in-law ▬▬▬▬▬▬▬▬▬

Read the pairs of guide words below. Then write the spelling words that you'd find on the page with each set of guide words.

cadet ▶ castle   mend ▶ mock   ballot ▶ boutique

_____   _____   _____

_____   _____   _____

B Test Yourself

For each item, read the clue to the meaning of a spelling word and the name of the language that spelling word comes from. Then write the spelling word.

1. bunch of flowers (*French*)
2. hopping animal (*Native Australian*)
3. place for snacks (*French*)
4. pasta (*Italian*)
5. stringed instrument (*Italian*)
6. food list (*French*)
7. gray-brown color (*French*)
8. old and priceless (*French*)
9. flower-like vegetable (*Italian*)
10. martial art (*Japanese*)
11. a dairy food (*Turkish*)
12. wax drawing stick (*French*)
13. instrument with keys (*Italian*)
14. pie (*Italian*)
15. place to eat meals (*French*)
16. classical dance (*French*)
17. bushy-tailed animal (*Algonquian*)
18. container (*French*)
19. green squash (*Italian*)
20. soft shoe (*Algonquian*)

For Tomorrow…
Get ready to share your observations about words from other languages. Remember to study for the test!

Get Word Wise

Karate is a Japanese word meaning "empty hands." This is a good name for this Japanese martial art form of self-defense, because no weapons are needed to defeat an opponent. The empty hands do it all!

Word Study Strategy

See the word

Say it slowly

Link sounds and letters

Write

Check

END

LESSON 32

Spelling Words

suspend
suspense
defend
defense LOOKOUT WORD
offend
offense LOOKOUT WORD
pretend
pretense
refer
reference
confer
conference
infer
inference
prefer
preference
perform
performance
insure
insurance

Review	Challenge
zucchini	interfere
restaurant	interference
certain	

My Words

_____

_____

_____

Verbs to Nouns

A See and Say

The Spelling Concept

Verb	Noun
confer	conference
perform	performance
defend	defense

The suffixes -ence and -ance are added to many verbs to form nouns. Sometimes the end *d* in the verb changes to *se* for the noun.

B Link Sounds and Letters

Say each spelling word. Listen for how the pronunciation changes from verb to noun. Then write the verb-to-noun pairs in the correct columns on a chart like this one.

It makes sense to remember ense in defense and offense.

MEMORY JOGGER

Word Sort

Add -ence		Add -ance		Drop e; then add -ance		Change d to se	
Verb	Noun	Verb	Noun	Verb	Noun	Verb	Noun

C Write and Check

What word means "to like better"? _ _ _ _ _ _

What is its noun form? _ _ _ _ _ _ _ _ _ _

Drop the first letter of each word. What two other spelling words do you get? _ _ _ _ _ and _ _ _ _ _ _ _ _ _

Now make up a word puzzle like the one above for two other spelling words.

_____

_____

A Build Vocabulary: **Word Meanings**

Write the verb that best fits each meaning.

1. to make believe
2. to give a show
3. to take out insurance
4. to attach something and let it hang down
5. to protect someone from harm

6. to look up information
7. to insult someone
8. to ask for advice
9. to like something better
10. to draw a conclusion

B Word Study: **Suffixes**

Finish this story about Jesse at the music auditions. Replace each underlined verb with its noun form. Remember to add the correct suffix.

11. Jesse could hardly stand the <u>suspend</u> as she waited to hear about the music audition.
12. She had already heard the orchestra's <u>perform</u> and knew she wanted to play in it.
13. The conductor told Jesse that Keith was always absent, so he made the <u>infer</u> that Keith no longer wanted to play.
14. Jesse spoke up in <u>defend</u> of Keith.
15. The conductor said that he would be attending a music <u>confer</u> the next week.
16. His <u>prefer</u> was to fill the orchestra position before leaving.
17. When Jesse finally heard the conductor's decision, she kept up the <u>pretend</u> of being happy.
18. She tried not to take <u>offend</u> at being turned down for the orchestra.

Spell Chat

With the person next to you, find another verb-to-noun pair. Here's one example: *reassure* and *reassurance*.

C Write

Write two short sentences for a business letter. Use the words *reference* and *insurance* in your sentences.

_____

_____

Be a Spelling Sleuth

In catalogs, instructions, and how-to manuals, look for verbs that become nouns. An example might be assure/assurance. Keep a list of words you find.

Spelling Words

suspend	confer
suspense	conference
defend	infer
defense	inference
offend	prefer
offense	preference
pretend	perform
pretense	performance
refer	insure
reference	insurance

Review	Challenge
zucchini	interfere
restaurant	interference
certain	

My Words

_____

_____

_____

Spelling Words

suspend	confer
suspense	conference
defend	infer
defense LOOKOUT WORD	inference
offend	prefer
offense LOOKOUT WORD	preference
pretend	perform
pretense	performance
refer	insure
reference	insurance

Review	Challenge
zucchini	interfere
restaurant	interference
certain	

My Words

_____

_____

_____

Quick Write

Imagine you're the new managing editor of your school's newspaper. Write a note to yourself, giving three suggestions to help in your new duties. Use at least two spelling words in your note.

A Write an E-Mail Message

 You can write your E-mail either on paper or on a computer. If possible, send your E-mail message.

You have just finished the year as a member of a school club. Write an E-mail message to a friend, describing a few highlights of the experience. Brainstorm a list of verb-to-noun word pairs to include in your E-mail message.

B Proofread

Ed just completed a year as a reporter for his school newspaper and wanted to send an E-mail message about it to his friend. He made four spelling mistakes, one capitalization mistake, and one punctuation mistake. Correct them.

Tip

When you end a declarative or an imperative sentence, use a period. End a question with a question mark. End an exclamation with an exclamation mark.

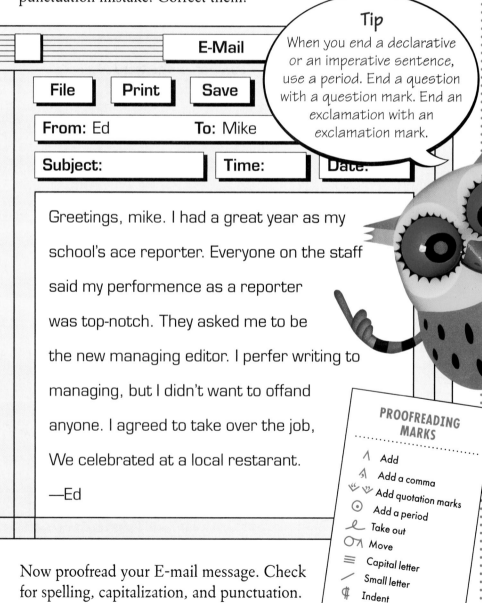

E-Mail

File   Print   Save

From: Ed   To: Mike

Subject: Time: Date:

Greetings, mike. I had a great year as my school's ace reporter. Everyone on the staff said my performence as a reporter was top-notch. They asked me to be the new managing editor. I perfer writing to managing, but I didn't want to offand anyone. I agreed to take over the job, We celebrated at a local restarant.

—Ed

PROOFREADING MARKS

∧ Add
⋏ Add a comma
⌄⌄ Add quotation marks
⊙ Add a period
ℓ Take out
○↗ Move
≡ Capital letter
/ Small letter
¢ Indent

Now proofread your E-mail message. Check for spelling, capitalization, and punctuation.

A Use the Dictionary:
Entry Words With Three Definitions

In a dictionary, definitions are numbered when more than one meaning is given. The most common meanings are often shown first, followed by the less common ones. Read this sample dictionary entry.

sus•pend /sə spend/

1. *verb* To attach something to a support so that it hangs downward. *We suspended the banner from the gym ceiling.* 2. *verb* To keep from falling as if attached from above. *The bee was suspended over the flower.* 3. *verb* To stop something for a short time. *School was suspended for the holiday.* ▷ **suspending, suspended.**

Write a sentence for each definition of the word *suspend*.

_____

_____

_____

B Test Yourself

Write the verb and noun form of each spelling word that belongs with the sets of words below.

1–2. imagine, make-believe

3–4. sing, concert

5–6. discuss, meeting

7–8. like, favorite

9–10. hurt, resentment

11–12. send to, informational book

13–14. make safe, protection

15–16. protect, guard

17–18. hang down, mystery

19–20. use reason, conclusion

For Tomorrow...
Bring your list of verbs-to-nouns to class, and compare it with a classmate's. Remember to study for the test!

Get Word Wise

Have you ever heard a suspenseful movie described as a "cliffhanger"? That term can help you see how the meanings of suspend and suspense are related. Suspend means "hang." When you're in suspense, you're left hanging. You don't know how a mysterious or dangerous situation will work out, and you're eager to learn the result.

Word Study Strategy

See the word

Say it slowly

Link sounds and letters

Write

Check

END

Spelling Words

scribe
script
scribble
describe
describing
descriptive
description
subscribe
subscriber
subscribing
subscription
prescribe
prescribing
prescription
scriptwriter
manuscript
transcribe
transcribing
transcription
transcript **LOOKOUT WORD**

Review	Challenge
offense	postscript
excellence	inscription
literature	

My Words

_____

_____

_____

Learn and Spell

Words With the Latin Root scribe

A See and Say

The Spelling Concept

scrib**ble**	to write carelessly and quickly
tran**scribe**	to make a written copy; to transfer
tran**script**	a written copy of a message or a report

Many English words are built on the Latin root *scribe*, which means "to write." Sometimes prefixes, suffixes, or both are added to *scribe* to make new words. This root is sometimes spelled *scrib* or *script*.

Shall I transcribe by transcription or prescribe by prescription?

MEMORY JOGGER

B Link Sounds and Letters

Say each spelling word aloud. Listen for the sound of the letter *i* in the root. When it sounds like long *i*, the root is spelled *scribe*. When it sounds like short *i*, it is usually spelled *scrib* or *script*. Sort your words on a chart similar to the one below.

Word Sort

The Root *scribe*	
Root Has Long *i* Sound	Root Has Short *i* Sound

C Write and Check

Complete this newspaper headline with spelling words.

**Man Orders Pharmacy _____ ,
Gets Magazine _____ Instead**

Now write your own headline with *scribe* words.

_____

_____

A Build Vocabulary: **Prefixes**

A prefix is a word part added to the beginning of a base word or root. Read each prefix below. Then combine the prefix with the root that means "to write" to create a spelling word. Write the new word.

de- means "down"

1. to write down so that people can see what you see
2. serving to describe
3. clearly pictured

trans- means "over"

4. to copy over in writing
5. a written copy
6. the act of writing a copy

manu- means "hand"

7. handwritten or typed pages

B Word Study: **Word Meanings**

Write a spelling word that is similar in meaning to the given phrase.

8. to write carelessly
9. a person who pays regularly for something
10. a magazine that arrives regularly in the mail
11. doctor's order for medicine
12. to write out an order for medicine
13. a person who copies words by hand
14. written text of a play or movie
15. to pay money to receive something regularly
16. someone who writes movies

C Writing

Use the following words in at least two sentences: *describing, prescribing, subscribing, transcribing.*

_____

_____

_____

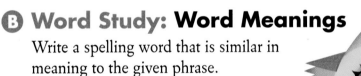

Be a Spelling Sleuth

Look through magazine and newspaper articles and advertisements to find five words with the Latin root scribe. Write the words you find.

Spell Chat

Turn to the person next to you, and brainstorm other words with the Latin root *scribe*.

Spelling Words

scribe	subscription
script	prescribe
scribble	prescribing
describe	prescription
describing	scriptwriter
descriptive	manuscript
description	transcribe
subscribe	transcribing
subscriber	transcription *LOOKOUT WORD*
subscribing	transcript

Review	Challenge
offense	postscript
excellence	inscription
literature	

My Words

_____

_____

_____

Spelling Words

scribe	subscription
script	prescribe
scribble	prescribing
describe	prescription
describing	scriptwriter
descriptive	manuscript
description	transcribe
subscribe	transcribing
subscriber	transcription
subscribing	transcript

LOOKOUT WORD

Review	Challenge
offense	postscript
excellence	inscription
literature	

My Words

_____
_____
_____

Quick Write

Imagine that you're the singer that Kam is interviewing. Write an answer to one of her questions. Use at least two of the spelling words.

A Write Interview Questions

You may wish to write your story on a computer.

You've just been given the best assignment ever—a chance to interview your favorite celebrity! Write five questions to ask him or her. Don't forget to use some spelling words.

B Proofread

Kam wrote some interview questions to ask her favorite singer. She made four errors in spelling, one in capitalization, and two in punctuation. Correct them.

Tip

Remember, a predicate adjective follows a linking verb and describes the subject. For example, *The flower smells good.*

> *Interview Questions*
>
> *1. Ms Sanchez, what was your life like in virginia when you were growing up? Please discribe it for me.*
>
> *2. Please give me a descripion of a typical day. Is it quiet now and then or do rehearsals fill all your time?*
>
> *3. You have achieved such a high level of excellance as a singer. Have you been approached by a scripwriters who wants to tell your story?*

PROOFREADING MARKS

∧	Add
⌃	Add a comma
∨∨	Add quotation marks
⊙	Add a period
ℓ	Take out
↶↷	Move
≡	Capital letter
/	Small letter
¶	Indent

Now proofread your own interview questions. Check spelling, capitalization, and punctuation. Underline predicate adjectives.

Ⓐ Use the Dictionary: **Etymology**

Most dictionaries give information about the sources of words—where they come from. Sometimes this information can be found right after the entry word. Often it can be found in special "Etymology" or "Word History" boxes on the page.

tran·script /tran skript/ *noun*

[L *transcribere* fr. *trans* + *scribere,* to write] a written, printed, or typed copy of dictated or recorded material

trans·crip·tion /tran skrip shən/ *noun*

[ME from ML *transcriptum* from L *transcriptus*] the act or process of transcribing written or recorded material

In the entries above, the *L* means "Latin," the *fr.* means "from," and the + means that two word parts were joined to make the entry word. *ME* means "Middle English," and *ML* means "Medieval Latin."

Read the following history for *scribe.*
What language does the word come from? _____
What did the word mean originally? _____

scribe [scrīb] *noun* [ME fr. L *scriba,* official writer]

Ⓑ Test Yourself

Write the spelling word hidden in each group of letters.

1. presubscribinger
2. redescribers
3. allsubscriptioning
4. audescriptivers
5. picscriptwriteral
6. bubscribblering
7. antranscribees
8. raprescriptionee
9. basscribe
10. seedescriptional
11. pasubscribertion
12. fitranscripton
13. lescripter
14. transcriptionting
15. demanuscriptear
16. represcribean
17. intranscribinger
18. ridescribingal
19. deprescribingly
20. masubscribear

For Tomorrow...
Share your list of sources for **scribe** words with a classmate. Remember to study for your test!

Do you know the difference between transcript and transcription? A transcript is a written record of dictated material. Transcription is the act or process of transcribing. Watch for these variations in spelling words.

Word Study Strategy

See the word

Say it slowly

Link sounds and letters

Write

Check

END

LESSON 34

Spelling Words

autograph
biography
biographer
biographical
autobiography
autobiographical
bibliography
photograph
photographer
photography
photographic
graphic
homograph
telegraph
telegram
diagram
monogram
program LOOKOUT WORD
grammar
grammatical

Review	Challenge
transcript	paragraph
patience	pictograph
telephone	

My Words

_____

_____

_____

Words With the Greek Roots graph, gram

Ⓐ See and Say

The Spelling Concept

photograph graphic photography

program grammar

Many English words are built on the Greek roots *graph* and *gram*, which relate to writing. Sometimes we add prefixes, suffixes, or both to these roots to make new words. Words with *graph* and *gram* are related in spelling and meaning.

My Grandma's grammar is always grammatical.

MEMORY JOGGER

Ⓑ Link Sounds and Letters

Say each spelling word. Listen for the Greek roots *graph* and *gram*. Look at the placement of the root in the word. Then sort the spelling words on a chart like this one.

Word Sort

graph_	_graph	_graph_	gram_	_gram

Ⓒ Write and Check

Complete these notes with spelling words.

Reminder:

✔ Must buy books at bookstore—a _____ of Michael Jordan and a _____ book of animal pictures taken on a safari.

Now write a reminder to yourself. Use at least two spelling words.

_____

_____

A Build Vocabulary: **Roots and Word Parts**

Look at the word parts and their meanings. Then read the definitions below. Write the spelling word that is formed by joining each of the following word parts with the roots *graph* and *gram*.

mono = "one" photo = "light" bio = "life"
auto = "self" tele = "far away" biblio = "book"

1. a written design made from one or more letters
2. a message sent far away
3. dealing with picture-taking by exposing film to light inside a camera
4. a person's handwritten signature
5. a written account of someone's life
6. someone who takes pictures by exposing film to light inside a camera
7. dealing with a written account of someone's life story
8. a list of books on a subject
9. a book in which someone tells his or her life story
10. one who writes another person's life story

B Word Study: **Word Meanings**

Read the word meanings below. Write a spelling word that goes with each one.

11. picture taken with a camera
12. the creation of pictures by exposing film in a camera to light
13. something written or drawn
14. system for sending messages far away
15. the rules of a language
16. having to do with language rules
17. a word that is spelled like another but has a different meaning
18. drawing or plan that explains something
19. radio or TV show
20. having to do with a book about oneself

Spelling Words

autograph	photographic
biography	graphic
biographer	homograph
biographical	telegraph
autobiography	telegram
autobiographical	diagram
bibliography	monogram
photograph	program
photographer	grammar
photography	grammatical

Review	Challenge
transcript	paragraph
patience	pictograph
telephone	

My Words

_____
_____
_____

Spelling Words

autograph	photographic
biography	graphic
biographer	homograph
biographical	telegraph
autobiography	telegram
autobiographical	diagram
bibliography	monogram
photograph	program
photographer	grammar *LOOKOUT WORD*
photography	grammatical

Review	Challenge
transcript	paragraph
patience	pictograph
telephone	

My Words

_____

_____

_____

Quick Write

You're Ms. Arnaz's sister, Rachel. You had to take care of Ms. Arnaz's dog for a year. Write two sentences about a funny thing the dog did. Use some spelling words.

Write and Proofread

A Write a News Article

You may wish to compose your newspaper article on a computer.

You have written the prizewinning biography of a woman who visited all 50 states in one year. Now write the highlights of the biography in a newspaper article telling *who, what, when, where,* and *why.* Use as many spelling words as you can.

B Proofread

Proofread the first paragraph of Dolores' news article. Find four errors in spelling, one error in capitalization, and two errors in punctuation.

> **Tip**
> Remember to use a colon between the hour and the minutes when you write the time. For example, *Dolores wakes up at 7:30.*

Rose Arnaz returned from her 50-state trip at exactly 4 05 last saturday afternoon. A journalist and a photografer met her at her door. Although she was tired, she described her trip with patiance. She even showed them a diagramm of her travel route. Then she slyly closed the door. "Thanks for your interest. You can find out more in my autobiografy.

PROOFREADING MARKS

∧	Add
⌃	Add a comma
⌄⌄	Add quotation marks
⊙	Add a period
ℓ	Take out
↶↗	Move
≡	Capital letter
/	Small letter
¶	Indent

Now proofread your news article. Check your spelling, capitalization, punctuation, and grammar.

Ⓐ Use the Dictionary: Respellings and Pronunciation

After every entry word in the dictionary, there is a respelling, or pronunciation, of the word. The dark type shows the accented, or stressed, syllable. The symbols that are used can be found in the dictionary's "Key." Respellings help you pronounce the words correctly. Look at the respelling of the word *autobiography*. Say the word.

au•to•bi•og•ra•phy /ô tō bī **og** rə fē/ *noun*
A book in which a writer tells his or her life story.

Write the respelling for each of these spelling words. Use the Spelling Dictionary for help.

program _____

biography _____

graphic _____

Ⓑ Test Yourself

Fill in the missing letters to make a spelling word.

1. gram _ _ _ _ _ _ _
2. gram _ _ _
3. p _ _ gram
4. m _ _ _ gram
5. d _ _ gram
6. h _ _ _ graph
7. graph _ _
8. t _ _ _ graph
9. t _ _ _ gram
10. _ _ _ _ _ graph _ c
11. _ _ _ _ _ graph _
12. _ _ _ _ _ graph _ r
13. _ _ _ _ _ graph
14. _ _ _ _ _ _ graph _
15. _ _ _ _ _ _ _ graph _ _ _ _

16. _ _ _ _ _ _ _ graph _
17. _ _ _ graph _ _ _ _
18. _ _ _ graph _ _
19. _ _ _ graph _
20. a _ _ _ graph

For Tomorrow...
Get ready to share the words you found in game instructions, advertisements, and computer programs. Remember to study for your test!

Get Word Wise

In ancient Greece, the word grammar meant not only "the study of language" but of literature as well. During the Middle Ages, few people could read or write, and the word grammar took on the meaning of "the rules of speaking or writing a language."

Word Study Strategy

See the word

Say it slowly

Link sounds and letters

Write

Check

END

Learn and Spell

Spelling Words

edit
editing
editor
edition
editorial
public
publicly *LOOKOUT WORD*
publicize
publicity
publicist
publication
publish
publisher
unpublished
journal
journalist
journalism
journey
column
columnist

Review	Challenge
grammar	commentator
assignment	commentary
notebook	

My Words

_____

_____

_____

Word Families

A See and Say

The Spelling Concept

publish - to have a book, newspaper, or magazine printed
publisher - one who produces a book, newspaper, or magazine
unpublished - not printed

Words that are formed from the same base word are related in spelling and meaning. Prefixes, suffixes, or both can be added to these base words to form new words.

The publicist publicly publicized her publication.

MEMORY JOGGER

B Link Sounds and Letters

Say each spelling word. Listen for the base word in each one. Then sort the words on a chart like this one.

Word Sort

Base Word	Related Words

C Write and Check

What spelling word is the opposite of *privately*? _ _ _ _ _ _ _ _

Write a sentence of your own that includes the answer to the question above and another spelling word.

_____

_____

_____

A Build Vocabulary: Suffixes

Read about each suffix. Then write the spelling word that matches each numbered item.

-ist, -er, and -or mean "one who"

1. one who publicizes
2. one who writes in a journal or newspaper
3. one who writes a column
4. one who publishes
5. one who edits

-ly means "in a manner"

6. in a public manner

-tion changes a verb to a noun

7. the product of editing
8. the product of publishing

-ity signals a noun

9. information given to the public

-ism means "the act or process of"

10. the act or process of a journalist

-ial can mark an adjective

11. having to do with editing a publication

-ize makes a noun into a verb

12. to make something public

Be a Spelling Sleuth

Look for words that share a base word, such as edition, edit, and editor, on newsstands, on billboards, and in the mail. Make a list of the words you find.

B Word Study: Related Words

Each of your spelling words is part of a word family, words that are related in meaning. Write the base word to which each of the words below is related.

13. reedit
14. republic
15. columnar
16. publishable
17. journals

Spell Chat

With a partner, come up with two word families of your own. Each family should include at least three words.

C Write

Write a sentence of your own that uses the spelling words *journey*, *unpublished*, and *editing*.

_____

_____

_____

Spelling Words

edit	publication
editing	publish
editor	publisher
edition	unpublished
editorial	journal
public	journalist
publicly *LOOKOUT WORD*	journalism
publicize	journey
publicity	column
publicist	columnist

Review	Challenge
grammar	commentator
assignment	commentary
notebook	

My Words

_____

_____

_____

Spelling Words

edit	publication
editing	publish
editor	publisher
edition	unpublished
editorial	journal
public	journalist
publicly	journalism
publicize	journey
publicity	column
publicist	columnist

Review	Challenge
grammar	commentator
assignment	commentary
notebook	

My Words

_____

_____

_____

Quick Write

You're Mr. Bluegill, owner of Bluegill's Hardware. Write two sentences to the students of Tyler Intermediate School expressing your admiration for their efforts and agreeing to invest in their work. Use some spelling words.

A Write a Persuasive Paragraph

 You may want to compose your persuasive paragraph on a computer.

You and some friends have a great idea—to start a school magazine. Everyone is helping out, but the group still needs money for start-up costs. Write a paragraph that persuades someone to invest in the project.

B Proofread

Proofread a draft of Jackie's persuasive paragraph. She made four spelling errors, one punctuation error, and two grammar errors. Correct her mistakes.

Tip
Be sure that singular verbs follow singular subjects and plural verbs follow plural subjects.

We want to publish a magazine just for Tyler Elementary students. No one know better than we do what kids are interested in. We already has expert editoral help, a proofreader to check our grammer, and several talented artists. Please make a publick investment in our magazine and help tomorrows journalists be publeashed!

Now proofread your own persuasive paragraph. Check your spelling, punctuation, and grammar. Pay close attention to the agreement of subjects and verbs in your sentences.

PROOFREADING MARKS

∧	Add
⅄	Add a comma
⌄⌄	Add quotation marks
⊙	Add a period
ℓ	Take out
↻	Move
≡	Capital letter
/	Small letter
¶	Indent

A Use the Dictionary: Stressed Syllables

Here's a dictionary entry word for *editorial*. The respelling shows boldface type for the heaviest-stressed syllable and italics for the second-heaviest stress. Remember, the syllable that is stressed the most is the one that is pronounced with more emphasis.

editorial /*ed* i **tôr** ē əl/

1. *adjective* To do with putting together a publication, as in *an editorial department.* **2.** *noun* An article or a statement that reflects the opinions of a newspaper or magazine editor or the managers of a television or radio station.

The spelling words below are divided into syllables. Say each word, and listen for stressed syllables. Write the word. Draw two lines under the syllable with the heaviest stress and one line under the syllable with the second-heaviest stress. Refer to your Spelling Dictionary if you need help.

pub li ca tion _____   pub lic i ty _____

B Test Yourself

Fill in the missing letters to make a spelling word.

1. ed _ _
2. public _ _
3. pub _ _ _
4. j _ _ _ _ _ l
5. j _ _ _ _ e _
6. journal _ _ t
7. public _ _ t
8. publ _ _ _ ti _ _
9. column _ _ _
10. _ _ publish _ _
11. e _ _ _ _ _ g
12. c _ _ u _ n
13. edit _ _
14. public _ _ y
15. journal _ _ m
16. public _ _ e
17. edit _ _ _
18. edit _ _ _ _ _
19. pub _ _ _ _
20. p _ _ li _ _ _ _

For Tomorrow...
Share the examples of related words you spotted on newstands, on billboards, and in the mail. Remember to study for your test!

Get Word Wise

The word journal was first used in ancient Rome as diurnalis, meaning "having to do with daytime." In medieval French journal meant "daily." Today, journal is "a book in which daily records are kept." Do you keep a daily journal?

Word Study Strategy

See the word

Say it slowly

Link sounds and letters

Write

Check

END

The Musician Who Loved to Cook ♪

Complete each paragraph with spelling words.

broccoli	autobiography	piano
bouquet	scribble	

Carlo Caratti, the famous musician, decided to write his **(1)** . He picked up a pen and started to **(2)** down some ideas. "I have two loves in my life," he wrote. "One is cooking tasty food, and the other is music. In fact, I love both so much that I keep a lovely **(3)** of **(4)** on my **(5)** . It inspires me when I play.

spaghetti	violin	zucchini	beige	publicly

"I can still remember when my first concert in the United States was **(6)** announced. I was going to play the **(7)** . I cooked long strands of **(8)** , which were luckily the same **(9)** color as my instrument's strings, and made a salad with fresh tomatoes and **(10)** . My friends laughed so hard when I broke a pasta "string" while I played!

pizza	journalist	photographer	infer
describing	description	publication	publish

"A **(11)** snapped a picture of me breaking the pasta string. That picture appeared in a national **(12)** . There was no **(13)** of my performance, but the **(14)** liked my sense of humor! Looking at the pasta and salad all over the stage, people might **(15)** that I was a chef instead of a musician. So then I thought, if so many people like my cooking, why not **(16)** a cookbook? I could include my recipe for great crusty **(17)** . I could even include a paragraph **(18)** how I bake a pizza and play the harmonica at the same time!

No Scribbling, Please!

The Latin root *scribe* means "to write." Write the spelling words that match each *scribe* definition below.

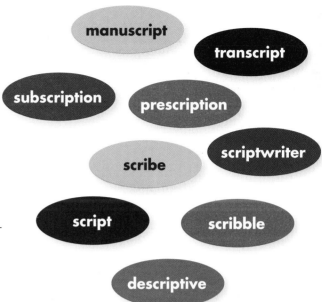

1. written text of a play _____

2. write carelessly _____

3. an order for magazines _____

4. writer of TV shows and movies _____

5. a written copy _____

6. person who copies books _____

7. doctor's written direction _____

8. handwritten or typed pages _____

9. serving to describe _____

Word Equations

Use these creative formulas to form spelling words. Add and subtract letters, and end up with words that are related to *public* and *graphic*.

publicly	**publicize**	**publicity**	**publication**
publisher	**photograph**	**telegraph**	**biography**

10. public + vacation - vac = _____

11. public + generalize - general = _____

12. public + husher - chu = _____

13. public + electricity - electric = _____

14. public + finally - final = _____

15. biology + graphy - logy = _____

16. television + graphic - vision - ic = _____

17. telephoto + graphic - tele - ic= _____

WORD PUZZLE

These four words are often confused. Use the definitions to solve the puzzle.

DOWN
1. team trying to score
2. protect from harm

ACROSS
3. make someone feel hurt
4. something that protects against harm

Start a Newspaper

Complete this application to work on the school newspaper. Use the spelling words from the box in your responses.

journalism   transcribe

journalist   photography

columnist   publish

editorial   edit

editing

Job Application

1. Name at least two jobs at the newspaper that you would like to do. Explain why each one interests you.

_____

_____

2. Name two jobs you would rather <u>not</u> do on the newspaper. Explain why each one does <u>not</u> interest you.

_____

_____

3. Tell us why you would be the best choice for the jobs you are applying for on the newspaper.

_____

_____

Tip
Remember to check subject-verb agreement in your sentences.

Look back at the words you misspelled on your Unit 6 Posttests and your My Words, Review Words, and Challenge Words. Use them to describe other useful skills to someone.

Tell About It

Write a letter about why you would or would not want to start your own newspaper or magazine. Proofread your work for spelling, capitalization, grammar, and punctuation.

PROOFREADING MARKS

∧ Add
⌅ Add a comma
⌄⌄ Add quotation marks
⊙ Add a period
ℓ Take out
↶↷ Move
≡ Capital letter
/ Small letter
¶ Indent

Write It Right!

Here are some words with the roots *graph* and *gram* that writers often confuse. Read each sentence. Then write the word that fits the meaning of the sentence.

- - - - - - - - - - - - - - **monogram   diagram** - - - - - - - - - - - - - - -

1. Steve had a _____ with his initials sewn onto his shirt.

- - - - - - - - - - - - - **autograph   graphic** - - - - - - - - - - - - - - -

2. The _____ on this page is a photo of our team.

- - - - - - - - - - - - **biography   bibliography** - - - - - - - - - - - - - -

3. Aretha had a long list of books called a _____.

- - - - - - - - - - - - - **autograph   graphic** - - - - - - - - - - - - - - -

4. The author gave me his _____ and also wrote a brief message in my book.

- - - - - - - - - - - - - **monogram   diagram** - - - - - - - - - - - - - - -

5. Peter drew a _____ so we could see where each room in the house was located.

- - - - - - - - - - - **biographical   autobiographical** - - - - - - - - - - -

6. Nahoko is writing an _____ account of her childhood in Japan.

Nathan says...

Everybody began collecting their books when the teacher made the last-minute assignment. I thought, "Wow, we're getting lots of work this weekend. I have to write a *biography*." I decided to write about my uncle who has traveled all over the world. Was I surprised on Monday when the teacher asked us for a *bibliography* for the science project we had just finished! All that work for nothing!

Spelling Matters!

A B C D E F G

H I J K L M N

O P Q R S T U

V W X Y Z

a b c d e f g h i j

k l m n o p q r s

t u v w x y z

absence	column	formerly	muscles	reign
accept	continue	fortunately	mystery	restaurant
aisle	convenience	further	mysterious	ruin
allegiance	courageous	grammar	nuclear	sense
ambulance	cruelty	heard	offense	several
argument	curiosity	heir	official	similar
author	defense	hospital	operator	scholar
behavior	describe	hour	outrageous	scientific
beige	description	icicle	particular	sculptor
bicycle	different	innocence	peculiar	sincere
boredom	doctor	instance	performance	situation
bouquet	edition	intelligence	picture	speech
breath	effect	its	pitcher	stationary
breathe	except	knew	preference	straight
broccoli	exercise	length	presence	strength
bruise	exhaust	liar	prescription	suspense
burglar	experience	lieutenant	principal	typical
byte	familiar	loyalty	principle	unfortunate
calendar	farther	mourning	publicly	vein
circumstance	finally	movable	refrigerator	wisdom

All your spelling words appear in alphabetical order in this Spelling Dictionary.
The labeled entry on this page shows you how to use the
Spelling Dictionary to find useful information about the words.

The **entry word** is the word you look up. This shows you how the word is divided into syllables.

This shows you how to pronounce the entry word. This word has two different **pronunciations.**

pro·gram /prō gram or prō grəm/

1. *noun* A television or radio show.
2. *noun* A schedule or plan for doing something.
3. *noun* A series of instructions, written in a computer language, that controls the way a computer works.
4. *verb* To give a computer instructions to make it do something.

from Greek: programma public notice

▶ **programming, programmed**

These are the **definitions** of the entry word. This word has four different meanings.

This tells you the **part of speech** of the entry word. Sometimes an entry word can be used as two or more different parts of speech.

These are other **forms** of the entry word. You might use them to check your spelling when you use the words in writing.

Other information comes after the definitions of some entry words. Here you might find the Greek or Latin origin of the entry word, or your Spelling Dictionary may mention another word that sounds the same.

A a

a·bil·i·ties /ə bil i tēz/ *noun, plural*
1. Powers to do something. *Pablo has many abilities that help him to succeed in school.* **2.** Skills.

a·bil·i·ty /ə bil i tē/ *noun*
1. Power to do something. **2.** Skill. *Millicent has great ability in art.*

ab·sence /ab səns/ *noun*
The state of being away or not present.

ab·sent /ab sənt/ *adjective*
Not present, away.

ac·cept /ak sept/ *verb*
To take something that is offered or given; to agree or consent to.

ac·ci·dent /ak si dənt/ *noun*
An unexpected event that often involves people being hurt.

ac·ci·den·tal /ak si den tl/
adjective Occurring by accident; not deliberate; unexpected.

ac·ci·den·tal·ly /ak si den tl ē/
adverb In an accidental way; randomly.

ac·cuse /ə kyoōz/ *verb*
To charge another with wrongdoing or committing a crime.
▶ **accusing, accused**

ac·tion /ak shən/ *noun*
Something to achieve a result or reach a goal.

ac·tive /ak tiv/ *adjective*
1. Energetic and busy, as in an *active* social life. **2.** Showing a verb's subject as doing something: *If I say, "I ran a mile," I am using the* active *voice.*

ac·tiv·i·ty /ak tiv i tē/ *noun*
1. A state of action or movement.
2. Something done to fill time; usually for pleasure. ▶ *plural* **activities**

ac·tor /ak tər/ *noun*
A person who performs in plays, movies, or on television.

ad·di·tion /ə dish ən/ *noun*
1. In math, the adding together of two or more numbers to reach a sum.
2. A section of a building added on to the original. **3.** Something new.

ad·mi·ra·ble /ad mər ə bəl/
adjective **1.** Worthy of being looked up to and modeled after. **2.** Excellent.

a·dult·hood /ə dult hoōd/ *noun*
The state of being a mature, fully grown person.

ad·vance /ad vans/
1. *verb* To move forward, to make progress. **2.** *verb* To lend money.
3. *adjective* Occurring before another event. *We received no advance warning of the test.*
▶ *verb* **advancing, advanced**

ad·van·ta·geous
/ad vən tā jəs/ *adjective*
Favorable; giving an advantage. *The sunny weather was advantageous to our picnic.*

af·fect /ə fekt/ *verb*
To influence, to change someone or something.

af·ford·a·ble /ə fôr də bəl/ *adjective* Available at a reasonable price.

air /âr/
1. *noun* The invisible mixture of gases that surrounds the Earth.
2. *verb* To freshen a room or house by letting in air.
Air sounds like **heir**.

aisle /īl/ *noun*
The passage between rows of seats.
Aisle sounds like **isle** and **I'll**.

al·le·giance /ə lē jəns/ *noun*
The loyalty given to one's country, government, cause, or another person or thing.

al·low·ance /ə lou əns/ *noun*
A specific amount of money given to someone on a regular basis.

al·pha·bet /al fə bet/ *noun*
The letters of a language arranged in their correct order.

Word History

Alphabet is derived from the first two letters of the Greek alphabet: *alpha* and *beta*.

al·pha·bet·i·cal
/al fə bet ə kəl/ *adjective*
Arranged according to the order of the alphabet, letter by letter.

a·maze·ment /ə māz mənt/
noun Great surprise; wonderment.
Synonym: astonishment

am·bu·lance /am byə ləns/
noun A vehicle that transports ill or injured persons to the hospital.

a·mi·go /ə mē gō/ *noun*
Spanish for "male friend." A female friend in Spanish is **amiga** /ə mē gə/.

an·i·mal /an ə məl/ *noun*
Any living creature that breathes, moves, and is not a plant.

an·tique /an tēk/
1. *noun* A very old object valued for its beauty and rarity. 2. *adjective* Very old and valuable.

ap·pear·ance /ə pēr əns/
noun The act of appearing, coming into sight. *The appearance of the sun lit up the darkened sky.*

ap·point·ment
/ə point mənt/ *noun*
1. The act of naming someone for a job or official position. 2. An arrangement to be somewhere or meet someone at a specific time.

ar·gue /är gyōō/ *verb*
1. To present an opinion on an issue or matter: *Phil will argue in favor of building a playground.*
2. To disagree strongly with another person.

ar·gu·ment /är gyōō mənt/
noun A discussion between people who disagree.

ar·ma·dil·lo /är mə dil ō/
noun A burrowing mammal covered by hard, protective plate found in southern North America and South America.

Word History

Armadillo means *the little armored one* in Spanish. It was so named by the Spanish explorers of North America who had never seen one before.

as·sign /ə sīn/ *verb*
To give someone a specific job or duty.
from Latin: signum mark or token

as·sign·ing /ə sīn ing/ *verb*
The act of giving someone a specific job or duty.

as·sign·ment /ə sīn mənt/
noun A specific task that is given to someone.
from Latin: signum mark or token

as·sist·ance /ə sis təns/ *noun*
Help or aid given by one person or persons to another.
Assistance sounds like **assistants**.

as·sist·ants /ə sis tənts/
noun, plural People who help someone else do a task or job.
Assistants sounds like **assistance**.

at·ten·dance /ə ten dəns/
noun The act of being present in a place or at an event.

at·trac·tion /ə trak shən/
noun 1. A thing or person that attracts or interests people. 2. The act or power of attracting or pulling something toward itself.

au·thor /ô thər/ *noun*
The writer of a book, play, article, poem, or any other literary work.

au·to·bio·graph·i·cal
/ô tə bī ə graf ə kəl/ *adjective*
Having to do with the story of someone's life.
from Greek: auto- self + bios made of life + graphein to write

au·to·bi·og·ra·phy
/ô tō bī og rə fē/ *noun*
A book in which the writer tells the story of his or her life.
▶ *plural* **autobiographies**

au·to·graph /ô tə graf/ *noun*
A person's signature.
from Greek: auto- self + graphein to write

au·to·mo·bile /ô tə mə bēl/
noun A passenger vehicle powered by an engine and usually having four wheels.
from Latin: auto- self + mobilis movable

a·ware·ness /ə wâr nəs/
noun The act of knowing or realizing something.

B b

bal·ance /bal əns/
1. *noun* The ability to remain steady and not fall over. 2. *verb* To keep something steady. 3. *verb* To weigh two things against one another on a scale.
▶ *verb* **balancing, balanced**

bal·let /bal ā or ba lā/ *noun*
1. A style of dance with precise, set movements. 2. A stage work that uses dance and music to convey a mood or tell a story.

bar·rel /bar əl/ *noun*
1. A large storage container, often made of wood. 2. The long tubelike part of a gun.

bas·es /bā sez/ *noun, plural*
1. Bottoms or supports of something. 2. Two or more of the four corners of a baseball diamond.

ba·sis /bā sis/ *noun*
The idea or reason behind something.

beg·gar /beg ər/ *noun*
A person who lives by asking for gifts.

be·have /bi hāv/ *verb*
1. To act in a proper, orderly manner. 2. To speak or act in a particular way. ▶ **behaving, behaved**

be·hav·ior /bi hāv yər/ *noun*
A way of acting or behaving.

beige /bāzh/ *noun*
A pale brown color.

be·liev·a·ble /bi lēv ə bəl/
adjective To feel that something is true. *Twana thought her cousin's story was believable.*

ber·ries /ber ēz/ *noun, plural*
Small, often brightly colored fruit found on bushes or trees.

ber·ry /ber ē/ *noun*
A small, often brightly colored fruit found on bushes or trees.
Berry sounds like **bury**.

be·wil·der·ment
/bi wil dər mənt/ *noun*
A confused state or condition.

bib·li·og·ra·phy
/bib lē og rə fē/ *noun*
A list of writings by a certain writer or about a subject.
from Greek: biblion- little book + graphein to write
▶ *plural* **bibliographies**

a	add	ô	order	th	this
ā	ace	o͞o	took	zh	vision
â	care	o͞o	pool		
ä	palm	u	up		
e	end	û	burn	ə	=
ē	equal	yo͞o	fuse	a	in *above*
i	it	oi	oil	e	in *sicken*
ī	ice	ou	pout	i	in *possible*
o	odd	ng	ring	o	in *melon*
ō	open	th	thin	u	in *circus*

bi·cy·cle /bī si kəl/ *noun*
A two-wheeled vehicle powered by foot pedals and steered with handlebars.

bi·og·ra·pher /bī og rə fər/ *noun* An author who writes about other people's lives.
from Greek: bios made of life + *graphein* to write

bi·o·graph·i·cal /bī ə graf i kəl/ *adjective* Concerning a person's life.

bi·og·ra·phy /bī og rə fē/ *noun* A book that tells about one person's life. ▶ *plural* biographies

bite /bīt/ *verb* To close your teeth around something. *Lindsay wanted to bite into the apple.* **Bite** sounds like **byte.**

bore·dom /bôr dəm/ *noun* Condition of finding people or events dull.

bou·quet /bō kā *or* boo kā/ *noun* A bunch of picked or cut flowers.

bou·tique /boo tēk/ *noun* A shop selling fashionable clothes or other specialty items.

breath /breth/ *noun* The air that you take into your lungs and breathe out again.

breathe /brēth/ *verb*
1. To draw air in and out of the lungs. 2. To whisper, say softly. *I didn't breathe a word to anyone.*
▶ breathing, breathed

bri·dal /brī dəl/ *adjective* Having to do with a bride or a wedding.
Bridal sounds like **bridle.**

bri·dle /brī dəl/ *noun* The straps that go around a horse's head and mouth and are used by a rider to control the horse.
Bridle sounds like **bridal.**

bril·liance /bril yəns/ *noun* The state or quality of being brilliant.

bril·liant /bril yənt/ *adjective*
1. Shining very brightly, as in *a brilliant diamond.* 2. Very smart. 3. Splendid or terrific, as in *a brilliant performance.*
▶ *adverb* brilliantly

broc·co·li /brok ə lē/ *noun* A green vegetable with stalks topped by rounded heads.

bruise /brooz/ *noun* A dark mark on the skin caused by broken blood vessels when a person falls or is injured.
▶ *verb* bruising, bruised

bur·glar /bûr glər/ *noun* A criminal who breaks into buildings and steals things.
▶ *noun* burglary

bur·ri·to /bər rē tō/ *noun* A tortilla, or Mexican pancake, rolled and filled with beef, chicken, or beans.

bur·ro /bûr ō/ *noun* A small donkey used as a pack animal.

byte /bīt/ *noun* A unit of information that is contained in a computer's memory.
Byte sounds like **bite.**

C c

ca·fé /ka fā/ *noun* A small restaurant.

cal·en·dar /kal ən dər/ *noun* A chart that shows all the days, weeks, and months of a given year.

can·yon /kan yən/ *noun* A deep, narrow river valley with steep, high sides.

cas·sette /ka set *or* kə set/ *noun* A flat, plastic container for recording tape, used to record and play sound and/or pictures.

cel·e·bra·tion /sel ə brā shən/ *noun* A joyous ceremony usually held to mark an important event.

change·a·ble /chān jə bəl/ *adjective* Capable of changing, varying.

child·hood /child hood/ *noun* The time during which someone is a child.

chi·li /chil ē/ *noun*
A hot spicy red pepper used in cooking.

cir·cu·lar /sûr kyə lər/ *adjective*
Shaped like a circle; round.

cir·cum·stance
/sûr kəm stans/ *noun*
The facts or conditions that are connected to an event, often plural.

clas·sic /klas ik/ *adjective*
1. Of very good quality and likely to remain popular for a long time, as in *classic novel.* 2. Typical. *This pair of sandals is a classic example of summer shoes.*

clas·si·cal /klas i kəl/ *adjective*
1. In the style of ancient Greece or Rome, as in *classical architecture.* 2. Traditional or accepted. 3. Timeless, as in *classical music* such as operas or symphonies.

clause /klôz/ *noun*
A group of words that contains a subject and a predicate and forms a sentence or part of a sentence. **Clause** sounds like **claws.**

claws /klôz/ *plural noun*
Hard, curved nails on the feet of animals and birds.
Claws sounds like **clause.**

clean·li·ness /klen lē nis/ *noun* The state of being clean.

cloud·i·ness /klou dē nis/ *noun* A cloudy condition.

clue /kloō/
1. *noun* A piece of information or evidence that helps find an answer to a question or a solution to a mystery. 2. *verb* To provide with necessary information. *Can you clue us in on what she said?*

clum·si·ness
/klum zē nis/ *noun*
Awkwardness; state of being clumsy.

co·in·ci·dence
/kō in sə dəns/ *noun*
A chance happening or meeting.

col·lec·tion /kə lek shən/
noun 1. A group of things collected over a period of time, often as a hobby. 2. Money gathered for a cause or purpose.

colo·nel /kûr nl/ *noun*
An officer ranking below a general in the armed forces.

co·lo·ni·al /kə lō nē əl/
adjective Concerning a colony or colonies.

col·umn /kol əm/ *noun*
1. A tall upright pillar supporting a building. 2. A row of numbers or words running down a page. 3. A piece of writing by one writer that appears regularly in a newspaper or magazine.

col·um·nist /kol əm nist/
noun A person who writes a column.

com·fort·a·ble
/kumf tə bəl/ *adjective*
1. Relaxed, feeling at ease.
2. Giving comfort, allowing to relax. ▶ *adverb* comfortably

com·men·tar·y
/kom ən ter ē/ *noun*
A description of and comments about an event or subject.

com·men·ta·tor
/kom ən tā tər/ *noun*
A person who delivers a commentary.

com·mo·tion /kə mō shən/
noun A state of noisy, excited activity.
from Latin: com- with + *movere* to move

com·pe·ti·tor
/kom pet i tər/ *noun*
A person who competes.
Synonyms: contestant, rival

com·pli·ca·tion
/kom pli kā shən/ *noun*
A complicated state that makes something difficult or confusing.

a	add	ô	order	th	this
ā	ace	oo	took	zh	vision
â	care	oo	pool		
ä	palm	u	up		
e	end	û	burn	ə	=
ē	equal	yoo	fuse	a	in *above*
i	it	oi	oil	e	in *sicken*
ī	ice	ou	pout	i	in *possible*
o	odd	ng	ring	o	in *melon*
ō	open	th	thin	u	in *circus*

con·duc·tor /kən duk tər/
noun **1.** A person who directs a group of musicians as it plays. **2.** A person whose job is to collect railroad fares. **3.** A substance through which heat, electricity, or sound can travel.

con·fer /kən fûr/ *verb*
1. To give someone a gift, an honor, or a reward. **2.** To hold a meeting with another person; to seek another's advice.
▶ **conferring, conferred**

con·fer·ence /kon fər əns or kon frəns/ *noun*
A formal meeting held to discuss ideas and opinions.

con·fi·dence /kon fi dəns/
noun **1.** Trust or firm faith in someone or something. **2.** A strong belief in one's own abilities.

con·tin·ue /kən tin yōō/ *verb*
To go on doing something.
▶ **continuing, continued**

con·tin·u·ous
/kən tin yōō əs/ *adjective*
To go on doing something without a break; unbroken.

con·tra·dict /kon trə dikt/
verb To say the opposite of or deny what someone else says.
from Latin: contra- against + *dictum* saying

con·tra·dic·tion
/kon trə dik shən/ *noun*
A statement that contradicts another statement: *There were several contradictions in his argument.*

con·ver·sa·tion
/kon vər sā shən/ *noun*
An informal talk between two or more people.

cor·rec·tion /kə rek shən/
noun The making of something right or accurate.

cour·age /kûr ij/ *noun*
Bravery, boldness, fearlessness.

cou·ra·geous /kə rā jəs/
adjective Having courage; unafraid.

cray·on /krā on or krā ən/
1. *noun* A colored wax stick used for drawing and coloring. **2.** *verb* To draw or color with a crayon.

crews /krōōz/ *noun, plural*
Teams of people who work together on a ship, an aircraft, or specific job.
Crews sounds like **cruise.**

crit·ic /krit ik/ *noun*
1. A person who finds fault with people or things. **2.** A person whose job is to review books, movies, plays, television programs, and so on.

crit·i·cal /krit i kəl/ *adjective*
1. Finding fault with someone or something. **2.** Serious or dangerous. *The patient was in critical condition.*

cru·el /krōō əl/ *adjective*
Deliberately causing pain to others or happy to see them suffer.

cru·el·ty /krōō əl tē/ *noun*
1. Hard heartedness. **2.** A cruel act or acts. ▶ *plural* cruelties

cruise /krōōz/
1. *noun* A vacation on a ship that docks at several places. **2.** *verb* To travel smoothly and easily.
▶ *verb* cruising, cruised
Cruise sounds like **crews.**

cu·ri·os·i·ty
/kyōōr ē os i tē/ *noun*
1. An eagerness to find out. **2.** A strange or rare object or creature. *Expression: "Curiosity killed the cat" means too much curiosity can get you into trouble.*
▶ *plural* curiosities

cu·ri·ous /kyōōr ē əs/ *adjective*
1. Eager to find out or learn. **2.** Strange, weird.

cur·rant /kûr ənt/ *noun*
1. A small raisin used in cooking.
2. A small, sour berry, used in making jelly.
Currant sounds like **current**.

cur·rent /kûr ənt/
1. *noun* The movement of water in a river or ocean or electricity through a wire. 2. *adjective* Happening now.
Current sounds like **currant**.

cym·bal /sim bəl/ *noun*
A musical instrument made of brass and shaped like a plate. It is played by striking it with a stick or another cymbal.
Cymbal sounds like **symbol**.

 D d

dan·ger /dān jər/ *noun*
1. An unsafe situation.
2. Something or someone that may cause harm or injury.

dan·ger·ous /dān jər əs/
adjective Likely to cause harm or injury; risky.

dark·ness /därk nis/ *noun*
State or condition of being dark or without light.

de·cent /dē sənt/ *adjective*
1. In good condition or satisfactory. 2. Respectable and proper. 3. Kind or thoughtful.

dec·o·ra·tion
/dek ə rā shən/ *noun*
1. Some things added to make prettier. 2. A medal or ribbon, given as an honor for something.

deep /dēp/ *adjective*
1. Going down a long way.
2. Very strong and intense.
3. Very low in pitch.

de·fend /di fend/ *verb*
1. To protect something or someone from harm. 2. To support someone or some action or idea by arguing.

de·fense /di fens or dē fens/
noun 1. A thing that protects or guards against harm. 2. A guarding against harm, defending. 3. Action or speech in favor of something.

dense /dens/ *adjective*
Crowded, or thick, as in *a dense fog*.

den·si·ty /den si tē/ *noun*
1. The heaviness or lightness of an object for its size. 2. The amount of something per unit. *The population density is greater in the Northeast.*

de·pend·a·ble
/di pen də bəl/ *adjective*
Reliable, can be depended on.

de·pend·ence
/di pen dəns/
noun Condition or state of being dependent, relying on someone or something else.

de·pend·ent /di pen dənt/
1. *noun* A person who is looked after and supported by somebody else. 2. *adjective* Depending on or controlled by someone or something else.

depth /depth/ *noun*
Deepness or a measure of deepness.

de·scent /di sent/ *noun*
1. Movement from a higher to a lower place. 2. A downward slope.

de·scribe /di skrīb/ *verb*
To create a picture of something or someone in words.
from Latin: de- down + *scribere* to write ▶ **described**

de·scrib·ing /di skrīb ing/
verb Creating a picture of something in words.

de·scrip·tion /di skrip shən/
noun 1. The telling in words how someone or something looks or acts. 2. An account that describes.

de·scrip·tive /di skrip tiv/
adjective Serving to describe.

de·sign /di zīn/
1. *verb* To draw something to be built or made. 2. *noun* The shape or style of something.
from Latin: de- down + *signum* mark, token

de·sign·er /di zī nər/ *noun*
A person who designs.

a	add	ô	order	<u>th</u>	this
ā	ace	o͞o	took	zh	vision
â	care	o͞o	pool		
ä	palm	u	up		
e	end	û	burn		
ē	equal	yo͞o	fuse	ə	=
i	it	oi	oil	a	in *above*
ī	ice	ou	pout	e	in *sicken*
o	odd	ng	ring	i	in *possible*
ō	open	th	thin	o	in *melon*
				u	in *circus*

de·sign·ing /di zī ning/
1. *adjective* Scheming. **2.** *noun* The art of making patterns, designs.

di·a·gram /dī ə gram/ *noun*
A drawing or plan that explains something.
from Greek: dia- through, across + *gramma* something written

di·a·ries /dī ə rēz/ *noun, plural*
Books in which people write down things that happen each day, either as a record or to plan ahead.

di·a·ry /dī ə rē/ *noun*
A book in which people write down things that happen each day, either as a record or to plan ahead.

dic·tate /dik tāt/ *verb*
1. To talk loudly and clearly so that someone can write down what you say. **2.** To control, give orders.
from Latin: dicere- to say + *-ate* to cause, to become

dic·ta·tion /dik tā shən/ *noun*
Words said or read aloud to another person who writes them down.

dic·ta·tor /dik tā tər/ *noun*
A person who has complete control of a country, often ruling it unjustly.

dic·tion·ar·y /dik shə ner ē/
noun A book that lists and defines words in a language in alphabetical order.
from Latin: dicere to say

dif·fer·ence /dif ər əns or dif rəns/ *noun*
1. The way in which things are unlike. **2.** The amount by which one number is less or more than another number.

dif·fer·ent /dif ər ənt or dif rənt/ *adjective*
Not the same.

dif·fi·cult /dif i kult/ *adjective*
1. Not easy, hard. **2.** Not easy to get along with, referring to a person.

dif·fi·cul·ty /dif i kul tē/ *noun*
A problem or obstacle.
▶ *plural* **difficulties**

di·rec·tion /di rek shən/ *noun*
1. The way that someone or something is moving or pointing. **2.** Guidance or supervision. *The play was under the direction of Mr. Rosen.*

di·rec·tor /di rek tər/ *noun*
A person in charge of directing a play, a movie, or a radio or television program.

dis·ad·van·tage /dis əd van tij/ *noun*
1. Something that causes a problem or makes life more difficult. **2.** Loss or damage. *The wet weather worked to the disadvantage of the outdoor event.*

dis·ap·pear·ance /dis ə pēr əns/ *noun*
The act of going out of sight, disappearing.

dis·ap·point·ment /dis ə point mənt/ *noun*
1. A letting down when you do not get what you wanted.
2. A person or thing that causes another's being disappointed.

dis·hon·or /dis on ər/ *verb*
To bring shame or disgrace upon yourself or others.
▶ *noun* **dishonor**

dis·hon·or·a·ble /dis on ər ə bəl/ *adjective*
Shameful, disgraceful.

dis·tance /dis təns/ *noun*
1. The space between two points or places. **2.** A place that is far away.

dis·tant /dis tənt/ *adjective*
1. Not close in space or time.
2. Not closely related. *Maria is my distant cousin.*

dis·turb·ance /di stûr bəns/ *noun* **1.** An interruption of normal activity. **2.** The thing that is disturbing.

diz·zi·ness /diz ē nis/ *noun*
A state of feeling unsteady or dizzy.

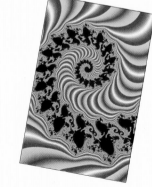

doc·tor /dok tər/ *noun*
1. A person trained and licensed to treat sick and injured people.
2. A person who earns the highest degree, a doctorate, given by a university.

do·nor /dō nər/ *noun*
1. A person who gives, or donates, possessions or money to a charity or organization. 2. A person who agrees to give his or her body, or part of it, to the cause of medical science.

drow·si·ness /drou zē nis/ *noun* A state of being drowsy; sleepiness.

E e

ed·it /ed it/ *verb*
1. To check a piece of writing for spelling, grammar, style, and factual errors, and shorten it if it is too long. 2. To cut and rearrange pieces of film, audiotape, or videotape to create a finished movie, television show, CD, etc.
▶ edited

ed·it·ing /ed it ing/ *verb*
1. Checking a piece of writing for spelling, grammar, style, and factual errors, shortening it if it is too long. 2. Cutting and rearranging pieces of film, audiotape, or videotape to create a finished movie, television show, CD, and so on.

e·di·tion /i dish ən/ *noun*
1. The form or version of a book or newspaper that is printed at one time. 2. The number of copies of newspapers, magazines, or books that are printed at the same time.

ed·i·tor /ed i tər/ *noun*
1. A person who checks the contents of a book and prepares it for publication. 2. A person in charge of putting out a newspaper or magazine.

ed·i·to·ri·al /ed ə tôr ē əl/
1. *adjective* Having to do with the putting together of a publication.
2. *noun* An article or a statement that reflects the opinion of a newspaper or magazine editor or the managers of a television or radio station.

ef·fect /i fekt/
1. *noun* The result or consequence of an action or cause. 2. *noun* Influence, or the power to make something happen. 3. *verb* To cause something to happen. *The president vowed to effect a change in education.*

e·lec·tion /i lek shən/ *noun* The act or process of choosing leaders or deciding on an issue by voting.

em·bar·rass·ment /em bar əs mənt/ *noun*
1. A condition of feeling awkward and uncomfortable. 2. A thing that causes a person to be embarrassed.

e·mo·tion·al /i mō shə nl/ *adjective* 1. To do with your feelings, as in *emotional problems*. 2. When someone becomes **emotional**, the person shows his or her feelings.
from Latin: ex- out of + *movere* to move

emp·ti·ness /emp tē nəss/ *noun* The state of containing nothing. *The emptiness of the room made Josie feel lonely.*

en·chi·la·da /en chə lä də/ *noun* A rolled tortilla filled with meat or cheese and served with a spicy sauce.

en·e·mies /en ə mēz/ *noun, plural* 1. People who hate and want to harm or destroy one another. 2. Countries or armies that you are fighting against in a war.

en·e·my /en ə mē/ *noun*
1. Someone who hates and wants to harm or destroy another. 2. A country or army that you are fighting against in a war.

en·joy·a·ble /en joi ə bəl/ *adjective* Giving pleasure or joy.

a	add	ô	order	ŧħ	this
ā	ace	o͝o	took	zh	vision
â	care	o͞o	pool		
ä	palm	u	up		
e	end	û	burn	ə	=
ē	equal	yo͞o	fuse	a	in *above*
i	it	oi	oil	e	in *sicken*
ī	ice	ou	pout	i	in *possible*
o	odd	ng	ring	o	in *melon*
ō	open	th	thin	u	in *circus*

en·joy·ment /en joi mənt/
noun 1. Pleasure; delight.
2. Having something as a benefit.
People who live in the United States have the enjoyment of personal freedoms.

e·nor·mi·ty /i nôr mi tē/ *noun*
Greatness or size of a job or task.
The enormity of the job made him feel exhausted.

e·nor·mous /i nôr məs/
adjective Extremely large.

en·trance /en trəns/
1. *noun* The way or doorway into a place. 2. /en trəns/ *verb* To give a feeling of wonder and pleasure.
▶ *verb* entrancing, entranced

en·tries /en trēz/ *noun, plural*
1. Ways into a place. 2. Pictures, stories, answers, etc. that you send into a competition. 3. Pieces of information in dictionaries, diaries, computers, and so on.

en·try /en trē/ *noun*
1. Way into a place. 2. Picture, story, answer, or such that you send into a competition. 3. Piece of information in a dictionary, diary, computer, and so on.

en·vel·op /en vel əp/ *verb*
To cover or surround something completely. *The house was enveloped in flames.*

en·ve·lope /en və lōp/ or /än və lōp/ *noun* A paper container for a letter or anything flat that is to be mailed.

e·qual /ē kwəl/
1. *adjective* The same as something else in size, value, or amount.
2. *adjective* The same for each member of a group. 3. *verb* To make or to do something the same as someone or something else.

e·qual·i·ty
/i kwol i tē/ *noun*
The same rights, values, amounts for everyone.

ex·act /ig zakt/ *adjective*
Perfectly correct, precise, and accurate.

ex·ag·ger·a·tion
/ig zaj ə rā shən/ *noun*
An exaggerated or overblown statement.

ex·am /ig zam/ *noun*
An official test of knowledge in a subject.
Exam is short for examination.

ex·am·ine /ig zam in/ *verb*
To look closely and carefully at something.
▶ examining, examined

ex·am·ple /ig zam pəl/ *noun*
1. One thing, animal, or person taken as typical of a larger group.
2. A person or thing held up as a model for others to imitate. 3. A question or problem given with its answer. 4. A warning to others.

ex·cel·lence /ek sə ləns/ *noun*
Being superior to all others, the finest quality.

ex·cel·lent /ek sə lənt/
adjective Very good, superior.

ex·cept /ik sept/
1. *preposition* Apart from.
2. *conjunction* But for the fact that.

ex·cite /ik sīt/ *verb*
To make someone eager or interested. ▶ exciting, excited

ex·cite·ment /ik sīt mənt/
noun 1. An excited state. 2. The thing that excites. *The excitement of riding a roller coaster is truly thrilling.*

ex·cuse /ik skyoos/
1. *noun* A reason given to explain why something went wrong.
2. /ik skyooz/ *verb* To give a person permission not to do something. 3. *verb* To forgive someone for doing something.
▶ *verb* excusing, excused

ex·er·cise /ek sər sīz/
1. *noun* Physical activity done to keep fit and healthy. 2. *verb* To perform physical activity in order to keep fit. 3. *noun* A task or piece of work done to practice a skill.
4. *verb* To put into practice. *Do you exercise your right to vote?*
▶ *verb* exercising, exercised

ex·haust /ig zôst/
1. *verb* To make very tired. 2. *verb* To use something up completely.
3. *noun* The waste gases produced by the running engine of a motor vehicle.

ex·hi·bi·tion /ek sə bish ən/
noun A public display of works of art, historical objects, and such.

ex·ist /ig zist/ *verb*
1. To live, or to have reality. 2. To have only a minimum of food to stay alive.

ex·it /eg zit or ek sit/
1. *verb* To leave or to go out.
2. *noun* The way out of a place.

ex·pand /ik spand/ *verb*
To increase in size; grow.

ex·pect /ik spekt/ *verb*
1. To wait for something to happen or someone to arrive.
2. To think or demand something from another person.

ex·pe·di·tion
/ek spi dish ən/ *noun*
1. A long journey with a serious purpose, such as exploring. 2. A short trip, usually recreational.

ex·pen·sive /ik spen siv/
adjective Costing a lot of money.
Antonyms: cheap, inexpensive

ex·pe·ri·ence
/ik spēr ē əns/
1. *noun* Something that happens to a person. 2. *verb* To happen to someone. 3. *noun* The knowledge and skill gained by doing something.
▶ *verb* experiencing, experienced

ex·per·i·ment
/ik sper ə mənt/
1. *noun* A scientific test to see the effects of something or to try out a theory. 2. *verb* To try something new.

ex·pert /ek spûrt/ *noun*
A person who is highly skilled at something or is highly educated about a particular subject.

ex·plain /ik splān/ *verb*
1. To make something clear so that it is easier to understand.
2. To provide a reason for something.

ex·plode /ik splōd/ *verb*
To burst apart or blow up with great force. ▶ **exploding, exploded**

ex·plor·er /ik splôr ər/ *noun*
A person who travels, or explores.

ex·port /ik spôrt or ek spôrt/
1. *verb* To send products abroad to be sold. 2. /ek spôrt/ *noun* The act of selling something to another country.
from Latin: ex- out of + portare to carry

ex·pose /ik spōz/ *verb*
1. To uncover something so it can be seen. 2. To reveal the truth about something or someone.
▶ **exposing, exposed**

ex·tra /ek strə/
1. *adjective* More than the normal amount. 2. *adverb* Extremely, or more than usual. 3. *noun* Something that is added, above and beyond the normal.

ex·treme /ik strēm/ *adjective*
1. Very great, strong. 2. Farthest.

F f

fair·ness /fâr nis/ *noun*
The state of being fair.

fame /fām/ *noun*
Being very well-known.

fa·mil·iar /fə mil yər/ *adjective*
1. Well-known; easily recognized.
2. Well-acquainted. *I am familiar with the game of chess.*

fa·mil·i·ar·i·ty
/fə mil ē ar i tē/ *noun*
To have knowledge about something, as in *to have familiarity with an author's books.*

fa·mous /fā məs/ *adjective*
Very well-known; celebrated.

far·ther /fär thər/
1. *adjective, adverb* A comparative of *far*. 2. *adverb* At a greater distance than something else.

fi·es·ta /fē es tə/ *noun*
A holiday or religious festival, especially in Spain and Latin America.

a	add	ô	order	th	this
ā	ace	oͬo	took	zh	vision
â	care	ōo	pool		
ä	palm	u	up		
e	end	û	burn	ə	=
ē	equal	yōo	fuse	a	in *above*
i	it	oi	oil	e	in *sicken*
ī	ice	ou	pout	i	in *possible*
o	odd	ng	ring	o	in *melon*
ō	open	th	thin	u	in *circus*

fi·nal·ly /fīn l ē/ *adverb*
At the end, last.

fine·ly /fīn lē/ *adverb*
1. Excellently done or made.
2. Thinly, delicately.

fit·ness /fit nis/ *noun*
The state of being fit or healthy.

flu·id /flōō id/ *noun*
A flowing substance, either a liquid or gas.

for·give·ness /fər giv nis/ *noun* The act of forgiving.

for·mal·ly /fôr məl lē/ *adverb*
Properly, not casually.

for·mer·ly /fôr mər lē/ *adverb*
In the past, or at an earlier time.

for·tu·nate /fôr chə nit/ *adjective* Lucky.

for·tu·nate·ly
/fôr chə nit lē/ *adverb* Luckily.

for·tune /fôr chən/ *noun*
1. Fate or destiny. 2. Chance or good luck. 3. A large amount of money.

Word History

Fortune is derived from the Latin word *fortuna*, meaning "fate" or "luck." The plural of the same Latin word, *fortunae*, means "possessions" or "goods" and hence, *fortune* today also means "riches."

---

fra·grance /frā grəns/ *noun*
A sweet or pleasing smell. *The flowers have a pleasant fragrance.*

fra·grant /frā grənt/ *adjective*
Having a sweet or pleasing smell. *It was a pleasure to walk in the fragrant garden.*

free·dom /frē dəm/ *noun*
The right to do and say what you like.

friend·ship /frend ship/ *noun*
The condition of being friends.

fruit /frōōt/ *noun*
1. The fleshy, juicy product of a plant that contains seeds and is usually edible. 2. The part of a flowering plant that contains seeds, such as a nut or a pod.

fu·el /fyōō əl/ *noun*
A source of heat or energy such as coal, wood, gasoline, natural gas, and so on. ▶ *verb* fuel

fu·ri·ous /fyōōr ē əs/ *adjective*
1. Extremely angry. 2. Fierce or violent.

fur·ther /fûr ᵺər/
1. *adjective, adverb* The comparative form of *far*. 2. *adverb* To a greater degree or extent.

fu·ry /fyōōr ē/ *noun*
Violent anger or rage.
▶ *plural* furies

G g

gar·den·er /gärd nər/ *noun*
1. A person who is hired to take care of gardens or lawns. 2. Any person who makes or works in a garden.

gen·tle·ness /jen tl nis/ *noun*
The quality of being kind, gentle.

glob·al /glō bəl/ *adjective*
1. Having to do with the world as a whole. 2. Shaped like a globe.

globe /glōb/ *noun*
1. The world, earth. 2. A round model of the earth. 3. Anything shaped like a round ball.

glo·ri·ous /glôr ē əs/ *adjective*
1. Having great fame or honor.
2. Magnificent, splendid.

glo·ry /glôr ē/ *noun*
1. Great fame or honor.
2. Something that brings great fame. 3. Splendor or magnificence. ▶ *plural* glories

gnu /nōō/ *noun*
A kind of African antelope with a large head, curved horns, and a long tail.
Gnu sounds like **knew** and **new**.

good·ness /good̄ nis/ *noun*
Generosity or kindness.

gov·ern·ment
/guv ərn mənt/ *noun*
1. The administration that runs a country, state, or organization. 2. The people who run or govern a country or state.

gram·mar /gram ər/ *noun*
The rules of speaking or writing a language.
from Greek: gramma- something written

gram·mat·i·cal
/grə mat i kəl/ *adjective*
Having to do with grammar.
Lucy made a grammatical error in her composition.

graph·ic /graf ik/ *adjective*
1. Strongly realistic; vivid. 2. Having to do with art and design. 3. Having to do with handwriting.
from Greek: graphein to write

grate /grāt/
1. *verb* To shred food into small, thin pieces. 2. *verb* To have an annoying effect. 3. *noun* A grid of metal bars in the base of a fireplace.
Grate sounds like **great**.
▶ **grating, grated**

great /grāt/ *adjective*
1. Very big or large. 2. Very important and famous. 3. Very good, wonderful.
Great sounds like **grate**.

gro·cer·ies /grō cə rēz/
noun, plural Food and other items sold at a grocery.

gro·cer·y /grō cə rē/ *noun*
A store that sells food and household goods.

H h

hap·pi·ness /hap ē nis/ *noun*
1. The state of being pleased and contented. 2. Good fortune.

heard /hûrd/ *verb*
Past tense and past participle of *hear*.
Heard sounds like **herd**.

heir /âr/ *noun*
A person who has been, or will be, left money, property, or a title by a relative.
Heir sounds like **air**.

herd /hûrd/
1. *noun* A large group of animals. 2. *verb* To make people or animals move together as a group.
Herd sounds like **heard**.

hik·er /hī kər/ *noun*
A person who goes on a long walk or hike.

him /him/ *pronoun*
The form of *he* used as a grammatical object.
Him sounds like **hymn**.

his·tor·i·cal /hi stôr i kəl/
adjective Having to do with people or events of the past.

his·to·ry /his tə rē/ *noun*
1. The study of past events. 2. A description of past events. *We are studying a history of California.*
▶ *plural* **histories**

hom·o·graph /hom ē graf/
noun One or two or more words that have the same spelling but different meanings. *Example:*
wave—a movement of water;
wave—to gesture
from Greek: homo- same + *graphein* to write

hon·est /on ist/ *adjective*
Truthful; will not lie, steal, or cheat.

hon·es·ty /on ə stē/ *noun*
Behavior that is truthful; the quality of being honest.
Expression: Honesty is the best policy.

hon·or /on ər/
1. *noun* A person's good reputation and the respect that other people have for him or her. 2. *verb* To give praise or an award. 3. *verb* To keep an agreement.

hon·or·a·ble /on ər ə bəl/
adjective 1. Good, deserving praise. 2. Keeping promises.

hon·or·a·bly / on ər ə blē/
adverb With honor, good grace.

a	add	ô	order	th	this
ā	ace	oo	took	zh	vision
â	care	ōō	pool		
ä	palm	u	up		
e	end	û	burn	ə	=
ē	equal	yōō	fuse	a	in *above*
i	it	oi	oil	e	in *sicken*
ī	ice	ou	pout	i	in *possible*
o	odd	ng	ring	o	in *melon*
ō	open	th	thin	u	in *circus*

hos·pi·tal /hos pi tl/ *noun*
A place where people receive medical treatment and are cared for when sick or injured.

hour /our/ *noun*
A unit of time equal to 60 minutes.
Hour sounds like **our**.

hu·mor /hyōō mər/ *noun*
1. The funny or amusing aspect of something. 2. A mood or state of mind.

hu·mor·ous /hyōō mər əs/
adjective Funny, amusing.

hymn /him/ *noun*
A song of praise to God.
Hymn sounds like **him**.

i·ci·cle /ī si kəl/ *noun*
A long, thin stem of ice formed from dripping water that has frozen.

i·dle /īd l/ *adjective*
1. Not busy, or not working.
2. Not active; not in use.
Idle sounds like **idol**.

i·dol /īd l/ *noun*
1. An image, or statue, worshipped as a god. 2. A person whom many people love and admire.
Idol sounds like **idle**.

ig·no·rance /ig nər əns/ *noun*
The state or fact of being ignorant; lack of knowledge or learning.

ig·no·rant /ig nər ənt/
adjective 1. Not aware of something. *I was completely ignorant of Ben's actions.* 2. Not educated, or not knowing about many things.

I'll /ī əl/ *contraction*
A short form of *I will* or *I shall*.
I'll sounds like **aisle** and **isle**.

im·port /im pôrt/ *verb*
To bring into a place or country.
from Latin: im- in, into + *portare* to carry

im·por·tance /im pôr tns/
noun The quality or state of being taken seriously, or importantly; significance.

in·cred·i·ble /in kred ə bəl/
adjective Unbelievable or amazing.
Jack's beanstalk grew to an incredible size.

in·de·pend·ence
/in di pen dəns/ *noun*
The condition of being free from the control of others; independent.

in·de·pen·dent
/in di pen dənt/ *adjective*
1. Free from the control of other people or things. 2. Self-reliant, not needing or wanting the help of others.

in·dus·tries /in də strēz/
noun, plural Manufacturing companies and other businesses. *Many steel and manufacturing industries are located near our town.*

in·dus·try /in də strē/ *noun*
1. Manufacturing companies and other businesses, taken together. *Our town needs more industry.*
2. A single branch of business or trade, as in *the tourist industry.*
3. Hard work or effort.

in·fer /in fûr/ *verb*
To draw a conclusion after considering all the facts.
▶ **inferring, inferred**

in·fer·ence /in fər əns
or in frəns/ *noun*
The process of drawing a conclusion from the facts.

in·flu·ence /in flōō əns/ *verb*
To have an effect on someone or something.
▶ **influencing, influenced**

in·for·ma·tion
/in fôr mā shən/ *noun*
Knowledge that comes from instruction or experience; facts about a specific subject or event.
Synonyms: knowledge, learning, data

in·her·it·ance /in her i təns/
noun Money or property received from ancestors.

in·no·cence /in ə sens/ *noun*
The state of being pure or uncorrupted.

in·scrip·tion /in skrip shən/
noun The act of inscribing or what is inscribed.
from Latin: in- in + *scribere* to write

in·sig·nif·i·cant
/in sig nif i kənt/ *adjective*
Trivial; not important.
from Latin: in- in + *signum* mark, token

in·spect /in spekt/ *verb*
To examine carefully.
from Latin: in- in + *spectare* to look

in·spec·tion /in spek shən/
noun The act of inspecting.

in·spec·tor /in spek tər/ *noun*
A person who inspects.
from Latin: in- in + *spectare* to look

in·stance /in stəns/ *noun*
An example; *for instance.*
Instance sounds like **instants.**

in·stants /in stəns/ *noun, plural*
Moments.
Instants sounds like **instance.**

in·struc·tions
/in struk shəns/ *noun*
Directions on how to do something or orders on what to do.

in·sur·ance /in shoŏr əns/
noun Paid protection from a company that agrees to pay money to a person in the event of sickness, fire, accident, or other loss.

in·sure /in shoŏr or in shûr/
verb To take out insurance.
▶ insuring, insured

in·tel·li·gence /in tel i jəns/
noun 1. Ability to learn and understand. 2. Information.

in·ter·fere /in tər fēr/ *verb*
1. To involve yourself in a situation that has nothing to do with you. 2. To hinder.
▶ interfering, interfered

in·ter·fer·ence
/in tər fēr əns/ *noun*
1. An unwelcome involvement in the affairs of others. 2. Something that interrupts a radio or television signal. 3. The illegal obstruction of an opponent in some sports.

in·ven·tion /in ven shən/ *noun*
1. The act or process of making something new. 2. A thing that is invented.

in·vi·ta·tion /in vi tā shən/
noun 1. The act of inviting. 2. The spoken or written manner in which a person is invited.

isle /īl/ *noun*
A small island.
Isle sounds like **aisle** and **I'll.**

it's /its/ *contraction*
A short form of *it is* or *it has.*
It's sounds like **its.**

its /its/ *adjective*
Related to or belonging to something.
Its sounds like **it's.**

J j

jan·i·tor /jan i tər/ *noun*
A person whose job is to look after and clean a building.

jour·nal /jûr nl/ *noun*
1. A diary in which a person writes down thoughts.
2. A magazine or newspaper.

jour·na·lism
/jûr nl iz əm/ *noun* The work of gathering and reporting news for newspapers, magazines, and other media.

a	add	ô	order	th	this
ā	ace	oŏ	took	zh	vision
â	care	ōō	pool		
ä	palm	u	up		
e	end	û	burn	ə	=
ē	equal	yōō	fuse	a	in *above*
i	it	oi	oil	e	in *sicken*
ī	ice	ou	pout	i	in *possible*
o	odd	ng	ring	o	in *melon*
ō	open	th	thin	u	in *circus*

jour·nal·ist /jûr nl ist/ *noun*
A person who collects information and writes articles for newspapers and other media.

jour·ney /jûr nē/ *noun*
A long trip ▶*verb* journey

joy·ous /joi əs/ *adjective*
Feeling, causing, or showing joy and happiness. *Allegra's birthday party was a joyous event.*

juice /jo͞os/ *noun*
Liquid that comes out of fruit, vegetables, or meat.

K k

kan·ga·roo /kang gə ro͞o/ *noun* An animal of Australia with short front legs and long, powerful back legs that are used for leaping. The female carries her young in a pouch for about six months after birth.

ka·ra·te /kə rä tē/ *noun*
A Japanese form of self-defense in which people fight each other using controlled kicks and punches.

kind·ness /kīnd nis/ *noun*
1. Being friendly, generous.
2. Kind treatment.

king·dom /king dəm/ *noun*
1. A country that has a king or queen as its ruler. 2. One of the main categories into which all living things are divided, such as the plant kingdom.

knead /nēd/ *verb*
To press, fold, and stretch something to make it smooth. **Knead** sounds like **need**.

knew /no͞o/ or /nyo͞o/ *verb*
Past tense of *know*.
Knew sounds like **gnu** and **new**.

L l

laugh /laf/ *verb*
To make sounds and movements to show a person thinks that something is funny.

laugh·ter /laf tər/ *noun*
The sound of laughing.

lea·der·ship /lē dər ship/
noun 1. The state of being a leader.
2. The ability to lead.

length /lengkth/ *noun*
1. The distance from one end of something to the other. 2. The amount or extent from the beginning to end.

lev·el /lev əl/
1. *adjective* Flat and smooth.
2. *adjective* At the same height. 3. *noun* A floor or story of a structure.
4. *noun* A height. 5. *noun* A position or rank in a series.

liar /lī ər/ *noun*
A person who doesn't tell the truth.

lib·er·ties /lib ər tēz/
noun, plural Freedoms.

lib·er·ty /lib ər tē/ *noun*
Freedom.

lieu·ten·ant /lo͞o ten ənt/
noun An officer of low rank in the armed forces.

lik·a·ble /lī kə bəl/ *adjective*
Popular.

like·ness /līk nis/ *noun*
A resemblance; similarity.

liv·a·ble /liv ə bəl/ *adjective*
1. Fit for living in. 2. Easy to live with.

lla·ma /lä mə/ *noun*
A large, South American mammal raised for its wool.

long /lông/
1. *adjective* More than an average length, distance, time, or such.
2. *adjective* From one end to the other. 3. *adverb* For a long time.

lov·a·ble /luv ə bəl/ *adjective*
Capable or worthy of being loved.

loy·al /loi əl/ *adjective*
Firm in supporting or faithful to one's country, family, friends, or beliefs.

loy·al·ty /loi əl tē/ *noun*
Faithfulness. ▶ *plural* loyalties

lu·nar /lo͞o nər/ *adjective*
Having to do with the moon.

mag·nif·i·cence
/mag nif ə səns/ *noun*
The state or quality of being impressive or splendid.

mag·nif·i·cent
/mag nif ə sənt/ *adjective*
Very impressive or splendid. *The king lived in a magnificent palace.*
▶ *adverb* magnificently

man·u·script
/man yə skript/ *noun*
1. The original handwritten or typed pages of a book or other writing before it is printed. 2. A handwritten document.
from Latin: man- hand + *scriptus* written

mem·ber·ship
/mem bər ship/ *noun*
State of belonging to a group.

men·u /men yo͞o/ *noun*
1. A list of foods served in a restaurant. 2. A list of choices shown on a computer screen.

me·sa /mā sə/ *noun*
A hill or mountain with steep sides and a flat top.

mis·for·tune /mis fôr chən/ *noun* 1. An unlucky event. 2. Bad luck.

mo·bile /mō bəl *or* mō bīl/
1. *adjective* Able to move.
2. /mō bēl/ *noun* A sculpture made of several items and hanging from a central wire or thread.
from Latin: mobilis movable

moc·ca·sin /mok ə sin/ *noun*
A soft leather shoe or slipper without a heel. Moccasins were originally worn by Native Americans.

mod·el /mod l/
1. *adjective* Small or miniature.
2. *adjective* Perfect or ideal.
3. *noun* Someone who poses for an artist or a photographer or wears clothing to show how it looks. 4. *noun* A thing or person who is a good example.

mo·lar /mō lər/ *noun*
A broad, flat tooth at the back of the mouth.

mon·o·gram /mon ə gram/ *noun* A design made from two or more letters, usually someone's initials.
from Greek: monos- single + *gramma* letter

morn·ing /môr ning/ *noun*
The time of day between sunrise and noon.
Morning sounds likes **mourning**.

mos·qui·to /mə skē tō/ *noun*
A small insect, the female of which bites and sucks blood from animals and humans.

mo·tion /mō shən/
1. *noun* Movement. 2. *verb* To tell someone something through a gesture.
from Latin: movere to move

mo·tor /mō tər/ *noun*
A machine that provides the power to make something run or work.

mo·tor·boat /mō tər bōt/ *noun* A boat powered by a motor, especially a small, open boat with an outboard motor.

mo·tor·cy·cle
/mō tər sī kəl/ *noun*
A heavy vehicle with two wheels and an engine.

mo·tor·ist /mō tər ist/ *noun*
Someone who travels by car.

mourn·ing /môr ning/ *noun*
1. The wearing of black to show grief over a person's death. 2. A draping of buildings, flying flags at half-mast, and so on, to show sorrow.
Mourning sounds like **morning**.

mov·a·ble /mo͞o və bəl/
adjective 1. Capable of being moved. 2. Capable of being carried from place to place.

a	add	ô	order	th	this
ā	ace	o͝o	took	zh	vision
â	care	o͞o	pool		
ä	palm	u	up		
e	end	û	burn	ə	=
ē	equal	yo͞o	fuse	a	in *above*
i	it	oi	oil	e	in *sicken*
ī	ice	ou	pout	i	in *possible*
o	odd	ng	ring	o	in *melon*
ō	open	th	thin	u	in *circus*

moz·za·rel·la
/mot sə rel lə/ *noun*
A soft, white cheese used in making pizza and other Italian foods.

mul·ti·pli·ca·tion
/mul tə pli kā shən/ *noun*
The process of adding the same number to itself several times.

mus·cles /mus əlz/ *plural noun*
Parts of the human body that pull on the bones to produce movement.
Muscles sounds like **mussels.**

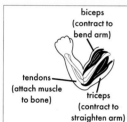

biceps
(contract to
bend arm)

tendons
(attach muscle
to bone)

triceps
(contract to
straighten arm)

mus·cu·lar /mus kyə lər/
adjective 1. Having strong, well-developed muscles. 2. Having to do with the muscles.

mu·sic /myoo zik/ *noun*
1. A pleasant arrangement of sounds that forms a musical composition. 2. The act of combining sounds in a pleasant way.

mu·si·cal /myoo zi kəl/
1. *adjective* Very interested in music or can play an instrument.
2. *adjective* Having to do with music. 3. *noun* A play or movie that includes singing and dancing.

mus·sels /mus əlz/ *noun, plural*
A type of edible shellfish.
Mussels sounds like **muscles.**

mus·tang /mus tang/ *noun*
A wild horse found mostly on the western plains of the United States.

mys·te·ri·ous /mi stēr ē əs/
adjective Very hard to explain or understand; strange.

mys·ter·y /mis tə rē/ *noun*
1. Something that is hard to explain or understand. 2. A story containing a puzzling crime that has to be solved. ▶ *plural* **mysteries**

N n

neat·ness /nēt nis/ *noun*
Quality of being orderly and clean.

need /nēd/
1. *verb* To want or require something urgently. 2. *noun* Something that you must have.
3. *verb* To have to do something.
4. *noun* A necessity or an obligation.
Need sounds like **knead.**

neigh·bor·hood
/nā bər hood/ *noun*
The local area around your home.

nerve /nûrv/ *noun*
1. One of the thin fibers that sends messages between the brain or spinal cord and another part of the body so it can move and feel.
2. Courage, daring.

nerv·ous /nûr vəs/ *adjective*
1. Easily upset or tense. 2. Fearful or timid. 3. Having to do with the nerves.

new /noo/ *adjective*
1. Just made or begun. 2. Seen, known, or thought of for the first time. 3. Not yet used to or experienced at. 4. Recently arrived in a place, position, relationship, or role. 5. Not yet worn or used.
New sounds like **gnu** and **knew.**

nor·mal /nôr məl/
1. *adjective* Usual or regular.
2. *adjective* Healthy. 3. *noun* The usual condition.

nov·el /nov əl/
1. *noun* A book that tells a long story about made-up people and events. 2. *adjective* New and unusual.

nu·cle·ar /noo klē ər/ *adjective*
1. To do with a nucleus, the central part of an atom. 2. To do with the energy created by splitting atoms, as in *nuclear power.*

nui·sance /noo səns/ *noun*
Someone or something that annoys you.

num·ber /num bər/
1. *noun* A word or symbol used for counting and for adding and subtracting. 2. A number that identifies someone or something, as in *a telephone number.* 3. *verb* To give a number to something. *Kenny numbered the index cards from one to ten.* 4. *verb* To amount to a number. *The crowd numbered at least 300.*

nu·mer·al /noo mər əl/ *noun*
A written symbol that represents a number.

nu·mer·ous /nōo mər əs/
adjective Many, or made up of a large number. *Sarah has made numerous friends at school.*

nu·tri·tion /nōo trish ən/ *noun*
The process by which food is taken and used by the body.

 O o

oc·ca·sion /ə kā zhən/ *noun*
1. A time when something happens. 2. A special or important event.

oc·ca·sion·al /ə kā zhə nl/
adjective Happening from time to time.

oc·cu·pa·tion
/ok yə pā shən/ *noun*
1. A job. 2. The taking over and controlling of an area by an army.

of·fend /ə fend/ *verb*
To make someone feel hurt.

of·fense /ə fens/ *noun*
1. A crime. 2. /ô fens/ In sports, the team that is attacking or trying to score. 3. The act of offending.

of·fice /ô fis/ *noun*
1. A room or building in which people work. 2. An important position.

of·fi·cial /ə fish əl/
1. *noun* A person who holds an important position in an organization. 2. *adjective* Approved by someone in authority.

op·er·a·tor /op ə rā tər/ *noun*
1. A person who works a machine or device. 2. A person who helps people make telephone calls.

or·na·ment /ôr nə mənt/ *noun*
A small, attractive object used as a decoration.

or·na·men·tal
/ôr nə men tl/ *adjective*
1. Used as a decoration or ornament. 2. Decorative.

our /ou´ər/ *pronoun*
Belonging to or to do with *us*.
Our sounds likes **hour**.

out·rage /out rāj/ *noun*
1. An act of violence or cruelty.
2. Extreme anger.

out·ra·geous /out rā jəs/
adjective Very shocking or offensive.

own·er·ship /ō nər ship/
noun The state of being a person who owns or possesses.

 P p

paint·er /pān tər/ *noun*
A person who paints pictures.

par·a·graph /par ə graf/
noun A short passage in a piece of writing that begins on a new line and is usually indented. A paragraph is made up of one or more sentences about a single subject or idea.

par·tic·u·lar /pər tik yə lər/
adjective 1. Individual or special.
2. Special. 3. Very careful about details.

pa·tience /pā shəns/ *noun*
Quality of putting up with problems and delays without getting angry or upset.
Patience sounds like **patients**.

pa·tients /pā shənts/
noun, plural People who are receiving treatment from a doctor or other health-care provider.
Patients sounds like **patience**.

pat·i·o /pat ē ō/ *noun*
A paved area next to a house, used for relaxing or eating outdoors.

pe·cu·liar /pi kyōol yər/
adjective Strange or odd.

per·form /pər fôrm/ *verb*
1. To do something or carry something out. 2. To give a show in public.

a	add	ô	order	ͭh	this
ā	ace	o͞o	took	zh	vision
â	care	o͞o	pool		
ä	palm	u	up		
e	end	û	burn	ə	=
ē	equal	yo͞o	fuse	a	in *above*
i	it	oi	oil	e	in *sicken*
ī	ice	ou	pout	i	in *possible*
o	odd	ng	ring	o	in *melon*
ō	open	th	thin	u	in *circus*

per·form·ance
/pər fôr məns/ *noun*
1. The public presentation of a play, movie, or piece of music. 2. The way in which someone or something performs.

per·spec·tive /pər spek tiv/
noun 1. A particular way of looking at a situation. 2. The way things or events relate to each other in size or importance.
from Latin: per- through + *spectare* to look or to see

pho·to·graph /fō tə graf/
noun A picture taken by a camera on film and then developed on paper. *from Greek: phot-* light + *graphos* written, writing

pho·tog·ra·pher
/fə tog rə fər/ *noun*
A person who takes photographs.

pho·to·graph·ic
/fō tə graf ik/ *adjective*
Having to do with or like photography.

pho·tog·ra·phy
/fō tog rə fē/ *noun*
The creation of pictures by exposing film inside a camera to light.

pi·an·o /pē an ō or pyan ō/
noun A large keyboard instrument that produces musical sounds when padded hammers inside the piano strike tuned metal strings.

pic·to·graph /pik tə graf/
noun A picture used as a symbol in ancient writing systems.

pic·ture /pik chər/ *noun*
1. An image of something, such as a painting, photograph, or drawing. 2. An image on a television, movie, or other kind of screen.

pi·ña·ta /pēn yä tə/ *noun*
A decorated container filled with candies and gifts. It is hung from the ceiling to be broken with sticks by children.

pin·to /pin tō/ *noun*
A horse or pony that has spots or patches of two or more colors.

pitch·er /pich ər/ *noun*
1. A container with an open top for liquids. 2. A baseball player who throws the ball to the batter.

piz·za /pēt sə/ *noun*
A flat pie that is baked with toppings of tomato sauce, cheese, and so on.

pla·za /plä zə or plaz ə/ *noun*
1. A public square. 2. An open area near buildings that often has walkways, trees, and benches.

plum /plum/ *noun*
A fruit that is soft when ripe and has a purple or yellow skin.

plumb /plum/
1. *verb* To examine or look closely at the nature or contents of something, as in *to plumb a mystery*. 2. *verb* To measure the depth of something. 3. *noun* A small, heavy object, usually made of lead, used to measure the depth of water.

plumb·er /plum ər/ *noun*
A person who puts in and repairs water and sewage systems.

po·lar /pō lər/ *adjective*
Having to do with or near the icy regions around the North or South Pole.

pop·u·lar /pop yə lər/
adjective 1. Liked or enjoyed by many people. 2. Having many friends. 3. Of or for the people.

port /pôrt/ *noun*
1. A harbor where boats and ships can dock or anchor safely. 2. A town or city with such a harbor.
from Latin: portus harbor

port·a·ble /pôr tə bəl/
adjective Able to be carried or moved easily.
from Latin: portare to carry

por·ter /pôr tər/ *noun*
A person who carries luggage or waits on people at a railroad station or hotel or on a train.

port·fo·li·o /pôrt fō lē ō/
noun A briefcase for loose papers, drawings, and such.
*from Latin: portare- to carry +
folio leaf of paper*

post·script /pōst skript/ *noun*
A short message beginning "P.S." that is added to the end of a letter, after the writer's signature.
from Latin: post- after + scribere to write

prance /prans/ *verb*
To walk or move in a lively or proud way. ▶ **prancing, pranced**

pred·a·tor /pred ə tər/ *noun*
An animal that lives by hunting other animals for food.

pre·dict /pri dikt/ *verb*
To say what you think will happen in the future.
from Latin: pre- before + dicere to say

pre·dic·tion /pri dik shən/
noun 1. The act of foretelling the future. 2. The thing predicted.

pre·fer /pri fûr/ *verb*
To like one thing better than another.

pref·er·ence /pref ər əns/
noun 1. Act of liking one thing better than another. 2. The thing preferred.

prep·a·ra·tion
/prep ə rā shən/ *noun*
1. A preparing, a getting ready, readiness 2. One or more things done to get ready.

pre·scribe /pri skrīb/ *verb*
1. To write what should be done. 2. To order as a medicine for a patient.
from Latin: pre- before + scribere to write ▶ **prescribed**

pre·scrib·ing /pri skrīb ing/
verb 1. Writing what should be done. 2. Ordering as medicine for a patient. *The doctor felt that prescribing more medicine for the patient was a good idea.*

pre·scrip·tion
/pri skrip shən/ *noun*
An order for drugs or medicine written by a doctor to a pharmacist.

pres·ence /prez əns/ *noun*
1. Being in a place at a certain time. 2. The area immediately near a person or thing.

pre·sent /pri zent/
1. *verb* To give someone a gift or prize. 2. /prez ənt/ *noun* A gift. 3. /prez ənt/ *noun* The time that is happening now. 4. /prez ənt/ *adjective* Being in a place; not absent.

pre·tend /pri tend/ *verb*
1. To make believe. 2. To claim falsely.

pre·tense /prē tens or
pri tens/ *noun*
1. Pretending. 2. A false appearance or show.

pride /prīd/ *noun*
1. A sense of your own importance or worth. 2. A too-high opinion of yourself.

prin·ci·pal /prin sə pəl/
1. *adjective* Most important, chief, or main. 2. *noun* The head of a public school.
Principal sounds like **principle**.

prin·ci·ple /prin sə pəl/ *noun*
1. A basic truth, law, or belief. 2. A rule that governs a person's behavior.
Principle sounds like **principal**.

pro·fes·sor /prə fes ər/ *noun*
A teacher of the highest rank at a college or university.

a	add	ô	order	th	this
ā	ace	o͞o	took	zh	vision
â	care	o͞o	pool		
ä	palm	u	up		
e	end	û	burn		
ē	equal	yo͞o	fuse	ə	=
i	it	oi	oil	a	in *above*
ī	ice	ou	pout	e	in *sicken*
o	odd	ng	ring	i	in *possible*
ō	open	th	thin	o	in *melon*
				u	in *circus*

Spelling Dictionary

pro·gram /prō gram or prō grəm/
1. *noun* A television or radio show.
2. *noun* A schedule or plan for doing something. 3. *noun* A series of instructions, written in a computer language, that controls the way a computer works. 4. *verb* To give a computer instructions to make it do something.
from Greek: programma public notice
▶ **programming, programmed**

pro·mote /prə mōt/ *verb*
1. To move someone to a more important job or to a higher grade in school. 2. To help with the growth or development of something.
from Latin: pro- forward + movere to move

pro·mo·tion /prə mō shən/
noun Advancement to a more important job or a higher grade in school.

proof /proof/ *noun*
Facts or evidence that something is true.

prop·er·ties /prop ər tēz/
noun, plural 1. Buildings and land that belong to someone. *Carl owns many properties throughout the city.* 2. Special qualities or characteristics of something, as in *the properties of water.*

prop·er·ty /prop ər tē/ *noun*
1. Anything that is owned by an individual. *Whose property is this?* 2. Buildings and land that belong to someone. *Two guard dogs stood watch over Janna's property.* 3. A special quality or characteristic of something, as in *the property of air.*

pros·pect /pros pekt/
1. *noun* Something that is looked forward to. 2. *noun* A view or a scene. 3. *verb* To explore or search for something, especially minerals.
from Latin: pro- forward + specere to see

pros·pec·tor /pros pek tər/
noun A person who explores a region in search of gold, silver, or other resources.

pro·tec·tion /prə tek shən/
noun 1. Act of keeping something safe from harm. 2. A person or thing that protects.

proud /proud/ *adjective*
1. Pleased and satisfied with what you or someone else has achieved.
2. Self-respect and a sense of your own importance. 3. Thinking too highly of yourself.

prove /proov/ *verb*
To show that something is true.
▶ **proving, proved**

pub·lic /pub lik/ *adjective*
1. To do with the people of the community. 2. Belonging to or being used by everybody.
3. Working for a form of government.

pub·li·ca·tion
/pub li kā shən/ *noun*
1. A book, magazine, or newspaper. 2. The production and distribution of a book, magazine, or other printed material.

pub·li·cist /pub lə sist/ *noun*
A person who writes and spreads information about a person or event to get the public's attention.

pub·lic·i·ty /pu blis i tē/ *noun*
Information about a person or an event that is given out to the public.

pub·li·cize /pub lə sīz/ *verb*
To make an event or person known to as many people as possible. ▶ **publicizing, publicized**

pub·lic·ly /pub lik lē/ *adverb*
1. Openly, before the public. 2. By the public.

pub·lish /pub lish/ *verb*
To produce and distribute a book, magazine, newspaper, or any other printed material for the public.

pub·lish·er /pub li shər/ *noun*
A person or company whose business is to publish books, newspapers, magazines, and such.

R r

rac·coon /ra koon/ *noun*
A mammal with rings on its tail and black and white face markings that look like a mask.

ra·di·a·tor /rā dē ā tər/ *noun*
1. A metal container through which hot liquid or steam circulates, sending heat into a room. 2. A metal device through which liquid circulates to cool a vehicle's engine.

rain /rān/
1. *noun* Water that falls in drops from clouds. 2. *noun* A falling of rain. 3. *verb* To fall in rain.
Rain sounds like **reign** and **rein**.

rapt /rapt/ *adjective*
Lost in something you enjoy so much you don't know what else is going on around you.
Rapt sounds likes **wrapped**.

read·a·ble /rē də bəl/
adjective 1. Interesting; easy to read. 2. Able to be read.

rea·son·a·ble
/rē zən ə bəl/ *adjective*
1. Fair. 2. Sensible. 3. Costing a fair price.

re·as·sign /rē ə sīn/ *verb*
To change a duty, office, or work assignment.
from Latin: re- again + *adsignare* assign

re·as·sign·ing
/rē ə sīn ing/ *verb*
Changing a duty, office or work assignment.

re·cent /rē sənt/ *adjective*
Happening, made, or done a short time ago.

rec·tan·gu·lar
/rek tang gyə lər/ *adjective*
Shaped like a rectangle with four sides and four right angles.

re·de·signed /re di zīnd/
verb Changed the shape and style of something.
from Latin: re- again + *designare* to mark out

re·fer /ri fûr/ *verb*
1. To look for information. 2. To mention something while talking or writing. 3. To send someone for additional or more detailed information. *My doctor has referred me to a specialist.*
▶ **referring, referred**

ref·er·ence /ref ə rens/ *noun*
1. A mention of someone or something. 2. A written statement about someone's character and abilities. 3. A book or magazine that you use to produce a piece of work.

re·frig·er·a·tor
/ri frij ə rā tər/ *noun*
A cabinet with a very cold interior, used for storing food and drink.

re·fuse /ri fyooz/
1. *verb* To say you will not do something or accept something. 2. /ref yoos/ *noun* Rubbish or trash. ▶ *verb* **refusing, refused**

re·gu·lar /reg yə lər/ *adjective*
1. Usual or normal. 2. According to habit or usual behavior. 3. Always happening or occurring at the same time.

reign /rān/ *verb*
To rule as a king or queen.
Reign sounds like **rain** and **rein**.

rein /rān/ *noun*
One of two straps attached to a bridle to control or guide a horse.
Rein sounds like **rain** and **reign**.

re·mark·a·ble
/ri mär kə bəl/ *adjective*
Worth noting; extraordinary.

re·mote /ri mōt/ *adjective*
1. Far away, isolated, or distant. 2. Extremely small or slight.
from Latin: re- back + *movere* to move

re·new·a·ble /ri noo ə bəl or ri nyoo ə bəl/ *adjective*
Capable of being extended, such as a library loan, club membership, and so on.

a	add	ô	order	th	this
ā	ace	oo	took	zh	vision
â	care	oo	pool		
ä	palm	u	up		
e	end	û	burn	ə	=
ē	equal	yoo	fuse	a	in *above*
i	it	oi	oil	e	in *sicken*
ī	ice	ou	pout	i	in *possible*
o	odd	ng	ring	o	in *melon*
ō	open	th	thin	u	in *circus*

re·port /ri pôrt/
1. *noun* A written or spoken account of something that has happened. 2. *verb* To give a report. 3. *verb* To make an official complaint.
from Latin: re- back + *portere* to carry

re·port·er /ri pôr tər/ *noun*
A person who gathers and reports the news.

re·sent /ri zent/ *verb*
To feel hurt or angry about something that has been done or said to you.

re·side /ri zīd/ *verb*
To live in a particular place for a long time. ▶ **residing, reside**

res·i·dent /rez i dənt/ *noun*
A person who lives in a particular place.

res·i·den·tial /rez i den shəl/
adjective Having to do with a neighborhood or an area where people live.

re·sign /ri zīn/ *verb*
To give up a job or a position voluntarily.
from Latin: re- back + *signum* mark

re·signed /ri zīnd/ *adjective*
Accepting something without concern or worrying about it.

re·sign·ing /ri zīn ing/ *verb*
Giving up a job, office, or position voluntarily.

re·spect /ri spekt/
1. *verb* To admire and have a high opinion of someone. 2. *noun* A feeling of admiration for someone.
from Latin: re- back, again + *specere* to look

res·tau·rant /res tər ənt or res tə ränt/ *noun*
A place where people pay to dine.

Word History

You may think that you go to a **restaurant** to eat, but the French word is derived from the verb *restaurer*, meaning "to restore or refresh." In France, dining is a relaxed, leisurely activity that can take hours and is meant to feed your spirit as well as your stomach!

re·us·a·ble /rē yoo zə bəl/
adjective Can be used again rather than thrown away.

ring /ring/
1. *noun* A circle. 2. *verb* To form a ring around. 3. *noun* A thin band worn on a finger as jewelry. 4. *verb* To make or cause to make a clear, musical sound. 5. *noun* A telephone call. 6. *noun* The area in which a boxing match takes place.
Ring sounds like **wring**.

ro·de·o /rō dē ō or rō dā ō/
noun A contest in which cowboys and cowgirls compete at riding wild horses and bulls.

role /rōl/ *noun*
1. The part that a person acts in a play. 2. The job or purpose of a person or thing.
Role sounds like **roll**.

roll /rōl/
1. *verb* To move along by turning over and over. 2. *verb* To make something into the shape of a ball or tube. 3. *verb* To flatten something by pushing a rounded object over it. 4. *noun* A round piece of baked bread dough.
Roll sounds like **role**.

rude /rood/ *adjective*
1. Not polite, as in *a rude answer* or *rude behavior*. 2. Roughly or crudely made. *In some countries, farmers still use rude wooden plows.* ▶ *adjective* **ruder, rudest** *adverb* **rudely**

ru·in /roo in/
1. *verb* To spoil or destroy something completely. 2. *noun* The destruction of something. 3. **ruins**, *noun, plural* The remains of something that has collapsed or been destroyed.

run·ner /run ər/ *noun*
1. A person who runs in a race. 2. The long, narrow part of an object that enables it to move or slide, as the blade on an ice skate.

S s

sad·ness /sad nis/ *noun*
The condition of being unhappy or sorrowful.

sail·or /sā lər/ *noun*
1. A person who works on a ship as a member of the crew. 2. A member of a country's navy.

sal·sa /säl sə/ *noun*
1. A hot, spicy tomato sauce. 2. A popular style of music that originated in Puerto Rico.

scents /sents/
1. *noun, plural* Pleasant smells. 2. *noun, plural* Liquids that are put on the skin to make it smell pleasant. 3. *verb* Starting to smell or feel that something is near. **Scents** sounds like **cents** and **sense.**

schol·ar /skol ər/ *noun*
1. A person who has a great deal of knowledge. 2. A serious student.

sci·ence /sī əns/ *noun*
1. The study of nature and the physical world by testing, experimenting, and measuring. 2. Any of the branches or fields of such study, such as biology.

sci·en·tif·ic /sī ən tif ik/
adjective 1. Using the laws or principles of science. 2. Having to do with science.

sci·en·tist /sī ən tist/ *noun*
A person who has expert knowledge or works in a branch of science.

scrib·ble /skrib əl/
1. *verb* To write or draw carelessly or quickly. 2. *verb* To make meaningless marks with a pencil, pen, or crayon.
from Latin: scribillare to write hastily
▶ **scribbling, scribbled**

scribe /skrīb/ *noun*
A person who copies books, letters, and other documents by hand.
from Latin: scriba public writer

script /skript/ *noun*
1. The written text of a play, a movie, or a television or radio show. 2. A form of writing in which the letters are joined together.
from Latin: scriptum something written

script·writ·er /skript rī tər/
noun A person who writes scripts for movies, television, or radio.
from Latin: scriba public writer

sculp·tor /skulp tər/ *noun*
An artist who produces sculpture, something carved or shaped out of stone, wood, or some other material.

se·lec·tion /si lek shən/ *noun*
1. The act of picking or choosing something. 2. A person or thing that has been chosen.

sense /sens/
1. *noun* One of the powers a living being uses to learn about its surroundings. Sight, hearing, touch, taste, and smell are the five senses. 2. *noun* A feeling. 3. *noun* Good judgment. 4. *noun* Meaning. 5. *verb* To feel or be aware of something.
Sense sounds like **cents** and **scents.** ▶ *verb* **sensing, sensed**

sen·tence /sen tns/ *noun*
1. A group of words that expresses a complete thought. 2. A punishment given to a guilty person.

sev·er·al /sev ər əl/
1. *adjective* More than two, but not many. 2. *noun* More than two, or a few, people or things.

sho·vel /shuv əl/
1. *noun* A tool with a long handle and a flattened scoop, used for moving material. 2. *verb* To move things with a shovel.

sick·ness /sik nis/ *noun*
1. Condition of being ill, sick. 2. A particular disease or illness.

si·es·ta /sē es tə/ *noun*
An afternoon nap or rest, usually taken after a midday meal.

a	add	ô	order	ŧℏ	this
ā	ace	o͞o	took	zh	vision
â	care	o͞o	pool		
ä	palm	u	up		
e	end	û	burn	ə	=
ē	equal	yo͞o	fuse	a	in *above*
i	it	oi	oil	e	in *sicken*
ī	ice	ou	pout	i	in *possible*
o	odd	ng	ring	o	in *melon*
ō	open	th	thin	u	in *circus*

sign /sīn/
1. *noun* A symbol that stands for something. 2. *noun* A public notice giving information. 3. *verb* To write your name in your own handwriting. 4. *noun* A trace left by someone.
from Latin: signum mark

sig·nal /sig nl/ *noun*
1. Anything agreed upon to send a message or warning.
2. One of many electric pulses transmitted for radio, television, or telephone communication.

sig·na·ture /sig nə chər/ *noun*
The unique way a person writes his or her name.
from Latin: signatura a signing

sig·nif·i·cance
/sig nif i kəns/ *noun*
1. Importance. 2. Meaning.
from Latin: significare to indicate

sig·nif·i·cant
/sig nif ə kənt/ *adjective* Important, or meaning a great deal, as in *a significant event.*

sig·ni·fy /sig nə fī/ *verb*
1. To be a sign, to represent.
2. To convey by signs or actions.
from Latin: significare to show by signs

sig·ni·fy·ing /sig nə fī ing/
verb Conveying by words or actions.

sign lan·guage
/sīn lang gwij/ *noun*
A language in which hand gestures, in combination with facial expressions and larger body movements, are used instead of speech. Sign language is often used by people with hearing impairments.

signpost /sīn post/ *noun*
A post with signs on it to direct travelers.

si·lence /sī ləns/
1. *noun* An absence of sound.
2. *noun* A keeping still. 3. *verb* To stop the speech or noise of.
▶ *verb* silencing, silenced

sim·i·lar /sim ə lər/ *adjective*
Alike, or of the same type.

sim·i·lar·i·ty /sim ə lar i tē/
noun The state of being similar, or alike.

sin·cere /sin sēr/ *adjective*
Honest and truthful in what a person says and does.

sin·cer·i·ty /sin ser i tē/ *noun*
Quality of being truthful; honesty.

sin·gle /sing gəl/
1. *adjective* One or no more than one. 2. *adjective* Intended for one person or family. 3. *adjective* Not married. 4. *noun* A hit in baseball that allows the runner to get to first base.

sin·gu·lar /sing gyə lər/ *noun*
The form of a word used for one thing or one person.

sit·u·a·tion /sich oo ā shən/
noun The circumstances that exist at a particular time.

sleight /slīt/ *noun*
1. Skill, cleverness. 2. A trick.
Sleight sounds like **slight**.

slight /slīt/
1. *adjective* Small or not very important. 2. *adjective* Slender.
3. *verb* To treat something as unimportant.
Slight sounds like **sleight**.

soft·ness /sôft nis/ *noun*
The quality of being soft.

so·lar /sō lər/ *adjective*
1. Having to do with the sun.
2. Powered by energy from the sun.

spa·ghet·ti /spə get ē/ *noun*
Long, thin strands of pasta made of flour and water and cooked by boiling.

speak /spēk/ *verb*
1. To talk out loud. 2. To tell your ideas, opinions, or feelings. 3. To deliver a speech. ▶ **speaking, spoke, spoken**

spe·cial /spesh əl/ *adjective*
1. Different or unusual.
2. Particular.

spe·cial·ty /spesh əl tē/ *noun*
1. A thing that someone is particularly good at. 2. A particular product or service.
▶ *plural* specialties

spec·i·men /spes ə mən/ *noun*
A sample, or an example used to stand for a whole group.
from Latin: specimen example

spec·ta·cles /spek tə kəlz/
noun, plural Eyeglasses.
from Latin: spectare to watch

spec·tac·u·lar
/spek tak yə lər/ *adjective*
Remarkable or dramatic.
from Latin: spectaculum show, sight

spec·ta·tor /spek tā tər/ *noun*
A person who watches an event and does not participate in it.
from Latin: spectare to watch

spec·u·la·tion
/spek yə lā shən/ *noun*
1. Act of guessing about something without knowing all the facts. 2. A conclusion or opinion reached by guessing.
from Latin: speculare to look out; examine

speech /spēch/ *noun*
1. The ability to speak. 2. A talk given to a group of people. 3. The way in which someone speaks.

star·dom /stär dəm/ *noun*
The state of being outstanding in some field.

state·ment /stāt mənt/ *noun*
1. Something that is said in words. 2. A list of all the amounts paid into and out of a bank or credit account.

sta·tion·ar·y /stā shə ner ē/
adjective 1. Not moving or not able to be moved. 2. Not changing.
Stationary sounds like **stationery**.

sta·tion·er·y /stā shə ner ē/
noun Writing materials, such as paper, envelopes, and pens.
Stationery sounds like **stationary**.

steal /stēl/ *verb*
1. To take something that does not belong to you. 2. To do something in a secret or tricky way.
▶ **stealing, stole, stolen**

stealth /stelth/ *noun*
Secret action.

straight /strāt/ *adjective*
1. Not bent or not curved. 2. Not curly or not wavy. 3. Not crooked or not stooping. 4. Level or even.
Straight sounds like **strait**.

strait /strāt/ *noun*
A narrow strip of water that connects two larger bodies of water.
Strait sounds like **straight**.
Idiom: In **dire straits** means you're in a very dangerous situation.

strength /strengkth or strenth/
noun 1. The quality of being strong. 2. The power to hold up under stress.

strong /strông or strong/
adjective 1. Powerful or having great force. 2. Hard to break; firm.

stu·dent /stōō dnt/ *noun*
A person who studies at a school.

stu·di·o /stōō dē ō/ *noun*
1. A room or building in which an artist or a photographer works. 2. A place where movies, television, or recordings are made.

sub·scribe /səb skrīb/ *verb*
To pay money regularly for a product or service.
from Latin: subscribere to write under, sign
▶ **subscribing, subscribed**

sub·scrib·er /səb skrī bər/
noun A person who pays money regularly for a product or service.

a	add	ô	order	ŧħ	this
ā	ace	ōō	took	zh	vision
â	care	oo	pool		
ä	palm	u	up		
e	end	û	burn		
ē	equal	yōō	fuse	ə	=
i	it	oi	oil	a	in *above*
ī	ice	ou	pout	e	in *sicken*
o	odd	ng	ring	i	in *possible*
ō	open	th	thin	o	in *melon*
				u	in *circus*

sub·scrib·ing
/səb skrīb ing/ *verb*
Paying money regularly for a product or service. *Jorge is subscribing to three newspapers.*

sub·scrip·tion
/səb skrip shən/ *noun*
1. A subscribing. 2. Money that is subscribed; a contribution.

sug·ges·tion /səg jes chən/
noun 1. Act of putting something forward as an idea or a possibility. 2. The thing suggested.

suit /sōot/
1. *noun* A set of matching clothes. 2. *noun* A case that is brought before a law court. 3. *verb* To be acceptable or convenient. *Does Monday suit you?*

sus·pect /sə spekt/ *verb*
To think that something may be true.
from Latin: suspectare form of *suspicere* to look up at

sus·pend /sə spend/ *verb*
1. To attach something to a support so that it hangs downward. 2. To stop something for a short time.

sus·pense /sə spens/ *noun*
An anxious and uncertain feeling caused by having to wait to see what happens.

sym·bol /sim bəl/ *noun*
A design or an object that represents something else. *On many maps, a small green pine tree is the symbol for a forest.* **Symbol** sounds like **cymbal**.

ta·co /tä kō/ *noun*
A Mexican food consisting of a folded fried tortilla filled with meat or cheese.

tai·lor /tā lər/
1. *noun* A person who makes clothes. 2. *verb* To design or alter something.

ta·ma·le /tə mä lē/ *noun*
A steamed Mexican dish consisting of meat rolled in cornmeal dough.

tel·e·gram /tel i gram/ *noun*
A message that is sent by telegraph.

tel·e·graph /tel i graf/ *noun*
A device or system for sending messages over long distances. It uses a code of electrical signals sent by wire or radio. The telegraph was invented by Samuel Morse in 1837.

tense /tens/ *adjective*
1. Nervous and worried. 2. Stretched tight, stiff. **Tense** sounds like **tents**.

tents /tents/ *noun*
Portable shelters made of canvas, supported by poles and ropes. **Tents** sounds like **tense**.

the·o·ries /thē ə rēz/
noun, plural 1. Ideas or statements that explain how or why something happens. *There are several theories about how the solar system was formed.* 2. Ideas or opinions based on some facts or evidence but not proved. *The police have two theories about who robbed the bank.*

the·o·ry /thē ə rē/ *noun*
1. Idea or statement that explains how or why something happens, as in *theory of evolution.* 2. Idea or opinion based on some facts or evidence but not proved. *The police have a theory about who robbed the bank.* 3. The rules and principles of an art or science, rather than its practice. *Meghan is taking a course in music theory.*

tor·til·la /tôr tē yə/ *noun*
A round, flat bread made from cornmeal or flour.

tran·scribe /tran skrīb/ *verb*
1. To copy in writing or typewriting. 2. To make a recording for broadcasting.
from Latin: trans- across + *scribere* to write ▶ **transcribed**

tran·scrib·ing
/tran skrīb ing/ *verb*
Making a written or typewritten copy of something. *Dexter is transcribing the minutes from our last club meeting.*

tran·script /tran skript/ *noun*
A written copy.

tran·scrip·tion
/tran skrip shən/ *noun*
The act of copying.

trans·port /trans pôrt/
1. *verb* To move people and freight from one place to another.
2. /trans pôrt/ *noun* A vehicle that carries people.
from Latin: trans- across + portare to carry

trans·por·ta·tion
/trans pər tā shən/ *noun*
A means or system for moving people from one place to another.

trav·el /trav əl/ *verb*
To go from one place to another.

trib·al /trī bəl/ *adjective*
Belonging to or of a group of people who share the same customs and laws.

tribe /trīb/ *noun* A group of people who share the same customs and laws.

Word History

Today **tribe** refers to any group of people with a common ancestry. Originally, the Latin word *tribus* referred to the three divisions of the ancient Roman people. The Latin root *tri* means "three" and also appears in such modern English words as *trio*, *triangle*, and *tricycle*.

true /trōō/ *adjective*
1. Agreeing with the facts.
2. Loyal. 3. Real.

truth /trōōth/ *noun*
The real facts.

tu·i·tion /tōō ish ən/ *noun*
Money paid to attend a private school or college.

tu·tor /tōō tər/
1. *noun* A teacher who gives private lessons to one student at a time. 2. *verb* To give private lessons.

type /tīp/
1. *noun* A kind or a sort. 2. *noun* Small pieces of metal used in printing. 3. *verb* To write with a typewriter or computer.
▶ *verb* typing, typed

typ·i·cal /tip i kəl/ *adjective*
Having traits or qualities that are normal for a type or class.

U u

un·der·stand·a·ble
/un dər stan də bəl/ *adjective*
Easy to grasp or understand.

un·for·get·ta·ble
/un fər get ə bəl/ *adjective*
So good, bad, or such that you will not forget it.

un·for·tu·nate
/un fôr chə nit/ *adjective*
Unlucky.

un·pub·lished /un pub lisht/ *adjective*
Not produced as a book, magazine, or final printed matter.

un·sci·en·tif·ic
/un sī ən tif ik/ *adjective*
Not according to the laws of science.

un·speak·a·ble
/un spē kə bəl/ *adjective*
1. Not able to be expressed in words. 2. Awful.

un·think·a·ble
/un thing kə bəl/ *adjective*
Out of the question.

a	add	ô	order	th	this
ā	ace	ōō	took	zh	vision
â	care	ōō	pool		
ä	palm	u	up		
e	end	û	burn	ə	=
ē	equal	yōō	fuse	a	in *above*
i	it	oi	oil	e	in *sicken*
ī	ice	ou	pout	i	in *possible*
o	odd	ng	ring	o	in *melon*
ō	open	th	thin	u	in *circus*

V v

vain /vān/ *adjective*
1. Conceited, proud.
2. Unsuccessful or futile.
Vain sounds like **vane** and **vein**.

val·ue /val yōō/
1. *noun* What something is worth.
2. *verb* To think that something is worthy. ▶ *verb* **valuing, valued**

vane /vān/ *noun*
A pointer that swings around to show the direction of the wind.
Vane sounds like **vain** and **vein**.

vein /vān/ *noun*
1. One of the vessels through which blood is carried back to the heart from other parts of the body.
2. One of the stiff, narrow tubes that form the framework of a leaf.
Vein sounds like **vain** and **vane**.

ver·dict /vûr dikt/ *noun*
The decision of a jury on whether an accused person is guilty or not guilty.

vic·tor·ies /vik tə rēz/
noun, plural A number of wins in a war or contest. *Rachel won many victories during her career as a tennis player.*

vic·tor·y /vik tə rē/ *noun*
A win in a battle or contest. *The tennis player held up her hands in victory when the game was over.*

vi·o·lin /vī ə lin/ *noun*
A stringed musical instrument, played with a bow.

vow·el /vou əl/ *noun*
A speech sound made with a free flow of air through the mouth. Vowels are represented by the letters *a, e, i, o, u,* and sometimes *y*.

W w

wash·a·ble /wosh ə bəl/
adjective Can be washed without causing any damage to material.

weak·ness /wēk nis/ *noun*
The condition of having little strength or power.

wide /wīd/ *adjective*
1. Having a certain distance from one side to the other. 2. Large from side to side. 3. Covering a large number of things.

width /width/ *noun*
The distance from one side of something to the other.

wil·der·ness /wil dər nis/
noun An area of wild land where no people live, such as a dense forest.

wis·dom /wiz dəm/ *noun*
Knowledge, experience, and good judgment.

wrapped /rapt/ *verb*
Covered with paper, material, and such.
Idiom: If you are **wrapped up** in something, you are totally involved in it.
Wrapped sounds like **rapt**.

wring /ring/ *verb*
1. To squeeze the moisture from wet material by twisting it with both hands. 2. To get by using force or threats.
Wring sounds like **ring**.

Y y

yo·gurt /yō gərt/ *noun*
A slightly sour food prepared from milk fermented by bacteria.

Z z

zuc·chi·ni /zōō kē nē/ *noun*
A kind of edible green squash shaped like a cucumber.